J A I M E   H

MECHANICS
(LOVE AND ROCKETS VOLUME TWO)
ISBN 1 85286 021 9

Published by Titan Books Ltd
58 St Giles High St London WC2H 8LH
First edition: May 1988
10 9 8 7 6 5 4 3 2 1

Designed by Rian Hughes

Printed and bound in Great Britain by
Richard Clays, Chichester, W Sussex

Mechanics

RNANDEZ

A
Love & Rockets

GRAPHIC NOVEL

TITAN BOOKS

CONTENT

JAIME HERNANDEZ was born in Oxnard, near Hollywood, California, in 1959, one of six brothers who were all encouraged to draw by their mother, herself a fan of comic books. He went on to study classical figure drawing at Ventura College in California, and to devour popular culture such as comics, pulp science fiction movies and rock music. However, it was punk together with the publication of the American *Heavy Metal* comic magazine that really made him realise that, creatively, anything was possible. Beginning in 1980 to draw from his own life he began to create the contemporary characters which people the fantastic but solidly urban reality of his *Love and Rockets* strips. These were self-published in a magazine of the same name also containing work by his brothers Gilbert and Mario, and a copy was sent to Gary Groth, the publisher of Fantagraphics' *The Comics Journal*. He immediately offered to publish their work regularly and, since then, *Love and Rockets* has grown in popularity on both sides of the Atlantic, being translated into four languages. With his brothers, Jaime has also drawn for the first four issues of *Mister X* (published during 1984 in Canada by Vortex Comics and collected into a single edition by Titan Books). Furthermore he has produced strips for *Silverheels*, *Vortex* and *Anything Goes*, along with poster pages for DC's *Who's Who* and pages for *The Rocketeer* graphic novel. Jaime continues to write and draw fifteen pages of *Love and Rockets* every eight weeks and plays drums in Gilbert and Carol Hernandez' new wave rock band, Nature Boy. He continues to live in Oxnard and is single.

s

11   Mechan-X

21   Mecánicos

29   Mechanics Part 1

35   Mechanics Part 2

41   Mechanics Part 3

47   Mechanics Part 4

53   Mechanics Part 5

60   Mechanics Part 6

71   Penny Century: On th' Road Ag'in Part 1

79   Penny Century: On th' Road Ag'in Part 2

89   The Lost Women Part 1

97   The Lost Women Part 2

107   The Lost Women Part 3

121   The Lost Women Part 4

131   The Lost Women Part 5

147   The Lost Women Part 6

At the climax of *Mechanics*, the title story of this second Titan Books collection of *Love and Rockets* tales by Jaime Hernandez, the beautiful Penny Century is leaning out of a helicopter that is pulling away from a dinosaur and an exploding rocket-ship in the depths of the South American jungle. What's more, she has just performed the death-defying, split-second rescue of her friend Maggie. You should also know that Penny's ambition is to become a superheroine and, since the richest man in the world, H R Costigan, is infatuated with her, this goal seems by no means unattainable; especially when you realise that Mr H R C has horns growing out of his cranium. It is at this point that Penny exclaims, 'Wow! That's the stuff comics are made of!'

INTRODUCTION

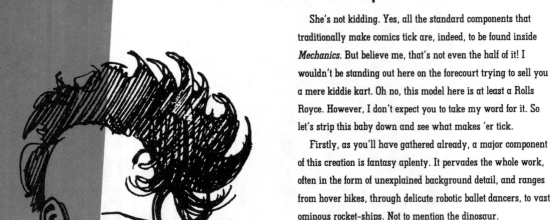

She's not kidding. Yes, all the standard components that traditionally make comics tick are, indeed, to be found inside *Mechanics*. But believe me, that's not even the half of it! I wouldn't be standing out here on the forecourt trying to sell you a mere kiddie kart. Oh no, this model here is at least a Rolls Royce. However, I don't expect you to take my word for it. So let's strip this baby down and see what makes 'er tick.

Firstly, as you'll have gathered already, a major component of this creation is fantasy aplenty. It pervades the whole work, often in the form of unexplained background detail, and ranges from hover bikes, through delicate robotic ballet dancers, to vast ominous rocket-ships. Not to mention the dinosaur.

Next, you'll notice a hefty charge of adventure: in strange locales, of course. We travel with the prosolar mechanics to wherever wrongs need to be righted. More precisely, and prosaically, we travel to where machines that have gone wrong need to be put right. These adventures are not beyond our wildest dreams, admittedly, but a realistically exciting prospect nevertheless. There's lots of action and all at its most tangible, too, from the basic fist in the face to the no-holds-barred, wide-screen extravaganza mentioned at the start.

Then, of course, we have the heroes and heroines. There's a wide choice of champions, from Rena Titañon, the charismatic woman wrestler, through to Rand Race, the hunky prosolar mechanic, with many stops in between.

To mention heroes is, naturally, to imply villains, and you won't be disappointed here either. The terrifying Torombolo, the creepy Doctor Beaky and the treacherous Yax Haxley are guaranteed to keep you hissing. Or, if you like to laugh, humour abounds, from the sly to the slapstick, the pun to the pratfall, and from steeltrap satire to deadpan irony.

Yes, Penny Century was right, the stuff that comics are made of is definitely present, all the time-tested mechanisms, the standard features and attractive bodywork we've come to expect. But look closer, and you'll find there's much more. There are hand-customised extras here, radical design innovations which transform the ride and make *this* baby run like a rocket.

I'd better let you in on a few secrets. You see, Penny isn't the only one in that helicopter. Margarita Luisa Chascarrillo is there, too, hanging on for dear life to Rand Race. She's just escaped death by a whisker but still has the presence of mind to cry 'Eek! Somebody turn the page! You can see my panties!'

Maggie (as her friends call her) is, you'll realise, altogether more modest and practical than Penny Century. It's not that she lacks strength of character or ambition; she wants to be a top prosolar mechanic. That's all, but that's plenty. As someone says of her, 'She doesn't need super-powers — she knows how to fix things'. In fact Maggie (as you'll call her too, once you've met her) is as close to being the heroine of this book as Penny is far from filling that role.

Similarly, in most other comics, Rand Race and his team of prosolar mechanics, all male bar Maggie, would be the most central and fully-realised characters. Here, however, they are ironically referred to as 'a big handsome guy, the old grumpy boss and, yes, even the country bumpkin!'

Meanwhile, Maggie's friends at home, whose part in the 'main' action is merely to read the letters in which she reports her exploits, are among the most subtly evoked characters you'll find anywhere in comics. They're quirky, endearing, irritating, unpredictable and elusive; they assume a reality which will keep them with you long after you've closed this book. As you may or may not be aware, these stories were first serialised in episodic magazine appearances. Collected together here in this volume, the personalities of Maggie and her friends blossom forth even more brightly in their full, comprehensively differentiated glory.

Now let's discuss the basic design. The fundamental difference of approach and emphasis from traditional comics in these stories is as drastic as when car designers realised that you could put the engine in a car *sideways* instead of lengthways. Someone suddenly saw that an internal combustion engine didn't have legs and a head, didn't have to face forward between shafts and, come to that, didn't eat hay. In short, that a car engine wasn't a *horse*.

Jaime Hernandez has wrought just such a basic and, after the fact, obvious change to the engineering of the comic strip. Fortunately for us, he has also had the knowledge and ability to construct the fully functioning prototype of his brilliant vision. For, whatever we may think that comics are composed of, it is the bonding of words and pictures that gives them substance and, in this ancient and obscure craft, Jaime has few peers.

Like all the best artefacts, Jaime's work has a handmade, informal feel to it. The frames are drawn freehand, the lettering is functional, the linework economical and every part has the stamp of a single hand using elementary tools. No production line or mechanical process has deadened this creation.

Perhaps only those of us who have laboured over the conveyor belts on the mainstream comics factory floor can fully appreciate what it takes to make something as good as this so simply. There's a saying in comics (and, I suspect, in other mass media): 'If you can't awe them with art, baffle them with bullshit.'

Well, there's no bullshit here, no over-rendering to conceal, or distract from, lack of skill. The sheer understanding distilled in each skilful line is almost supernatural. Indeed, it is art concealing art, so sophisticated in its translation of reality into graphic terms as to be genuinely awesome. Just look, for instance, at his subtle use of shadow.

The very innocence of the surface is beguiling and attractive. It assumes no familiarity with the coded ritualism of mainstream comic art, and is so easy to swallow that we can immediately start digesting the substance of the work. It is thus the perfect vehicle for the stories which Jaime Hernandez has to tell. And what magnificent stories they are!

Stories of hope and innocence, love and loss, heroism, and plain humanity, all recounted with an unaffected eloquence which is the equal of the masterly drawings. Jaime Hernandez allows his tales to unfold at their own pace, unfettered by constraints of page count or other commercial requirements. Like all the best creators, he imbues his characters with their own life and becomes, himself, invisible. His creation really is a perfectly functioning mechanism, twinkling in perpetual motion.

Now, I don't know if you've ever actually taken a complicated machine apart and then tried to re-assemble it. If you have, you'll know it's an immutable law of the universe that you always have a piece left over. It'll always be the most important part, without which the whole device just won't work. So, there it is, gleaming in splendid solitude on our work bench, a unique and vital part. With all this talk of machines and components, it seems a little elementary and incongruous. You see, it's just a chunk of plain, common-or-garden *love*. Corny? Yes, but look. This love is a love of the comics medium, with all its most grotesquely inbred characteristics, a love of drawing and love of a good story well told. Above all, it is the simple love of humanity, with all *its* most grotesquely inbred characteristics. For all the technology and hard-edged style within these pages, it is affection and goodwill that emanates from them, softening the hardness of the machinery. Love can, indeed, overcome rockets.

Jaime Hernandez patently knows exactly the stuff that comics are made of and, more importantly, he knows how the stuff fits together. Prosolar mechanics, eat your hearts out.

Now, quickly, somebody turn the page! You can see my panties!

Dave Gibbons,
November 1987.

OTHER TITLES
BY
THE HERNANDEZ
BROTHERS

Heartbreak Soup (by Gilbert Hernandez)
Duck Feet — Heartbreak Soup Volume Two (by Gilbert Hernandez)
Love and Rockets (by Jaime Hernandez)
The Return of Mister X

MECHAN-X STARRING maggie RACE hopey BY IZZY RUEBENS

GOODY... TIME FOR WORK... I'LL PROBABLY BE LATE AGAIN... MR. GHOUL WILL YELL THE EYES OFF ME... EMBARRASS ME IN FRONT OF THE OTHER WORKERS... BUT, WHO CARES? HA HA... OHH...

MAGGIE! WHAT ARE YOU DOING?

GOING TO WORK, HOPEY...

WORK? NOW? SHIT, YOU JUST GOT TO BED TWO FUCKING HOURS AGO! YOU CAN'T GO TO WORK LIKE THIS!

BUT, I GOTTA GO TO WORK...

HOPEY! LEGGO! I GOTTA GO TO WORK! THEY NEED ME... THEY... MY HEAD... I THINK I DRANK TOO MUCH LAST NIGHT! OHH...

LOOK AT YOURSELF, MAGGOT! I'LL BET YOU WOULDN'T EVEN MAKE IT TO THE BUS STOP! C'MON! SLEEP SOME...

PONTIAX SCXCH

BUT, I JUST GOTTA GO TO WORK! I DON'T WANNA GET FIRED! THIS IS MY THIRD JOB THIS MONTH! OOH... LOOK AT THE BAGS UNDER MY EYES...I'M FAT AGAIN... AND MY HAIR... ICK!

COULDN'T YOU SKIP AT LEAST ONE DAY?

I'VE ALREADY SKIPPED TOO MANY DAYS! OOH, I CAN'T STAND THIS SHITTY JOB! I CAN'T STAND ANY OF MY STALE JOBS! I HATE DOING STUFF I CAN'T DO!

MAGGIE! SOMETIMES YOU'RE SO DAMN STUPID IT'S PITIFUL! WHY DON'T YOU GO BACK TO YOUR MECHANIX JOB? THAT'S WHAT YOU'RE BEST AT!

YOU CAN FIX ANYTHING! WHO KNOWS, MAYBE ONE DAY YOU'LL EVEN BECOME A PROSOLAR MECHANIC! JUST LIKE RAND RACE, YOU'LL GET A MILLION BONES FOR ONLY FIXING THE KING OF ZHATO'S HEARING AID! THEN, YOU COULD BECOME A RICH, FAT SLOB!

I NEED A HAIRCUT! WILL YOU CUT MY HAIR, HOPEY? I NEED ONE AWFUL BAD!

FRAM DAMN IT! OK! IF I CUT YOUR FUCKIN' HAIR, WILL YOU QUIT PLAYING YOUR SILLY-ASS GAMES AND GO BACK TO BEING A MECHANIC? HOW? TODAY? OKAY?!!

OK! OK! I'LL DO IT! JUST GET OFF! YEOW!

HOPEY, THAT SLUT! I TOLD HER, OVER AND OVER, "DON'T CUT IT TOO SHORT IN THE BACK!" BUT NO, WHAT DOES SHE DO? NOW I LOOK MORE LIKE DEREK CINEMA THAN A FOTO MATE! OH WELL... NOW, AT LEAST I HAVE AN IMPORTANT JOB...

FIXING BROKEN EQUIPMENT ON THIS MILITARY BASE! ALAS, WE ALL GOTTA START ON THE BOTTOM! RIGHT NOW I HAVE TO WORK ON TAKYO WIRES! THAT'LL BE A CINCH!

15

LOOK! IT'S AN OLD ROBOT STORAGE SHACK! THEY HAVEN'T USED ROBOTS HERE SINCE THE WAR!

OKAY IF WE STOP AND LOOK AROUND, BOSS?

OH, PLEASE? I NEVER HAVE HAD THE CHANCE TO WORK ON A REAL ROBOT! BESIDES, WE'RE NOT DUE BACK FOR ANOTHER HOUR! PLEASE MR. MORALES, PLEEZE?

HOKAY, LITTLE GIRL! PULL OVER, RACE!

MY GOD, THIS IS INCREDIBLE! REAL METAL MEN!

YEAH! THEY PROBABLY EVEN STILL WORK! TAKE A LOOK AROUND! SINCE WE'RE HERE, WE'RE GONNA CHECK OUT THE GRINN SLACKS!

OOH, THIS LOOKS SIMPLE ENOUGH! I CAN HAVE ONE OF THESE STARTED AND FOLLOWING ORDERS IN NO TIME!

AND THAT'S JUST WHAT YOU'RE GONNA DO, FAT ASS!

NO STUPID, I'M NOT RACE'S PARTNER! THE REAL YAX HAXLEY'S TIED UP IN SOME CLOSET WITH THE HOLY SHIT KICKED OUT OF HIM! Y'SEE, I DON'T LIKE MY VICTIMS FIGHTING BACK! NOW, WHAT I WANT YOU TO DO FOR ME, IS TO KEEP YOUR FUCKING TRAP SHUT AND START THIS TIN CAN UP TO OBEY ME! AND NO TRICKS, HAH? NOW, GO TO IT, WHORE!

HEY! WATCH OUT!

OH, CHRIST! WHAT THE HELL IS SHE DOING IN THERE?!

THIS THING'S GONE LOCO FOR ME! YEOWCH!

CHASCARRILLO! GET YOUR BUNS OUT HERE! YAX!

RACE! DEACTIVATE IT WITH YOUR BALTAZORS!

GOOD IDEA!

16

25

MECHANICS

DEAR HOPEY,

SURPRISE! IT'S ME! I'M STILL ALIVE. I'LL BET YOU THOUGHT I WAS DEAD OR KIDNAPPED OR SOMETHING. WELL, I'M NEITHER. I'M WRITING FROM AN OLD, DECREPIT HOTEL CLEAR ACROSS THE GLOBE IN ZIMBODIA!! IT WAS REALLY WEIRD, LAST FRIDAY WHEN YOU AND IZZY WENT TO MAD-DOG'S WITHOUT ME, I WAS SITTING THERE ALL SENTIDA WATCHING TV WHEN THE PHONE RANG. IT WAS RAND RACE. HE SAID WE HAD A BIG, BIG JOB SOMEWHERE OUTSIDE OF THE COUNTRY AND THAT I HAD TO BE AT THE AIRPORT IN FIFTEEN MINUTES. SORRY I DIDN'T LEAVE A NOTE, BUT I BARELY HAD TIME TO EVEN PACK (I DIDN'T HAVE ENOUGH CLEAN UNDERWEAR, SO I BORROWED SOME OF YOUR OLD ONES, OK?). I'LL BET YOU THOUGHT I GOT SO SENTIDA THAT NIGHT THAT I WENT OUT AND KILLED MYSELF, HUH?

I'M SO EXCITED, BECAUSE WE'RE JUST STOPPED HERE FOR A NIGHT. WE REALLY HAVE TO GET TO, GET THIS... ZHATO.!! AND I DON'T MEAN THE FUN, POPULATED, CITY ZHATO, I MEAN THE JUNGLE, WILD ANIMALS, CANNIBALS ZHATO. IT'S SOME BIG GOVERNMENT JOB WE'RE ON. I'M NOT EVEN SURE IF I'M ALLOWED TO TELL YOU ABOUT IT. ESPECIALLY SINCE YOU'RE THE MOST ANTI-GOVERNMENT PERSON I KNOW. YOU'RE EVEN ANTI-ANTI (HA HA).

I'LL ONLY BE GONE FOR ABOUT A WEEK, SO IF YOU COULD PLEASE FEED TIC TAC AND WASH THE DISHES THIS WEEK AND I'LL DO THEM NEXT WEEK.

OH YEAH, AND PLEEEEEZZZ...

(OVER)

TAKE OUT THE TRASH, OK? THANKS A LOT. SEE YOU IN ABOUT A WEEK.

   LOVE YOU,
   MAGGIE

P.S. I'VE FINALLY SEEN A REAL LIVE ZIMBODIAN. THEY REALLY DO HAVE SKIN LIKE OLIVES. THEY ALSO HAVE THE BIGGEST FEET IN THE WORLD. § WHEW §

P.S.S. SAY HI TO IZZY AND PENNY FOR ME AND I'LL BRING YOU ALL SOUVENIERS FROM ZHATO REAL SOON.

DEAR HOPEY,

TODAY WE ARRIVED AT THE BUBÉ (PRONOUNCED BOO-BEH) AIRPORT JUST OUTSIDE ZHATO. WE'LL BE SPENDING THE NIGHT IN THE JUAN PANADERO HOTEL (UGH, WHAT A DUMP) BEFORE WE TAKE A CHOPPER INTO THE JUNGLE WHERE WE'LL BE WORKING. THERE WE MET THIS FUNNY GUY WHO WAS SUPPOSED TO FILL US IN ON WHERE WE WERE STAYING AND STUFF LIKE THAT, BUT HE DIDN'T KNOW HIS ASS FROM HIS SHIT. WE WAITED AROUND FOUR HOURS BEFORE WE GOT ANY INSTRUCTIONS. IT WASN'T SO BAD WAITING BECAUSE THEY HAD THIS LITTLE JUKE BOX IN THE AIRPORT CAFÉ AND ON IT WAS THE THEME SONG TO THAT HILLBILLY PROGRAM YOU LIKE. I PLAYED IT EIGHT TIMES. OH YEAH, I SAW A PICTURE OF THE DAMAGES ON THE ROCKET SHIP WE WILL BE FIXING, AND I HAVE A SLIGHT FEELING WE'LL BE MORE THAN A WEEK (WHAT A MESS). I'LL WRITE YOU IN A COUPLE OF DAYS. TAKE CARE, HAH?

   LOVE YOU,
   MAGGIE

P.S. THIS IS THE BUBENESE GREETING: "BUBÉ, BUBEBE BU." THAT MEANS, "DON'T COUNT YOUR CHICKENS BEFORE YOUR BRITCHES IS HATCHED." HA HA.

P.S.S. IN CASE YOU HAVEN'T NOTICED, OUR JOB IS TO FIX A ROCKET THAT CRASHLANDED IN THE JUNGLE YEARS AGO.

DAY 1

WELL, HERE WE ARE. SORRY I'VE TAKEN SO LONG TO WRITE, BUT WE HAVE TO GO ABOUT NINETY MILES INTO ZHATO TO MAIL A LETTER AND THE EXPRESS HERE IS SO SLOW. BUT ANYWAY, REMEMBER WHEN I TOLD YOU WE WERE WORKING IN THE DEEP JUNGLE? WELL, EVEN I DIDN'T KNOW IT WOULD BE THE DEEP, DEEP, DEEP, JUNGLE WHERE THE LOCAL NATIVE LANGUAGE IS SO COMPLEX THAT EVEN THE CLOSEST TRIBES WHICH ARE SEVERAL MILES AWAY CAN'T MAKE IT OUT.

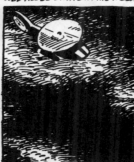

I MEAN, THIS JUNGLE IS SO DEEP, THAT IF THE ROCKET WE HAVE TO FIX DIDN'T OPEN SOME SPACE WHEN IT CRASHLANDED, WE'D ALL BE LIVING IN THE TREES.

OUR HUTS ARE VERY NICE. THEY'RE JUST LIKE THE ONES IN THE MOVIES, ONLY THEY SMELL JUST LIKE KAKA. I GUESS I'LL JUST HAVE TO GET USED TO THE STENCH HERE IN LOWER PELLUCIDAR. I MEAN, THIS JUNGLE IS SOOOOO DEEP THAT NEXT TO THIS BIG, BIG, BIG ROCKET SHIP WE HAVE TO FIX THAT IS STUCK IN THE SLIMEY MUCK, IS A BIG, BIG, BIG, OLD, FAT, SMELLY, FAT, OLD, BLACK DINOSAUR!

NO KIDDING. IT KIND OF LOOKS LIKE A BRONTOSAURUS REX EXCEPT IT'S GOT A BUMP ON IT'S HEAD. THEY SAY IT'S BEEN SITTING THERE SINCE THE BIG, BIG BIRD OUT OF THE SKY (THE ROCKET SHIP) CRASHED INTO IT MANY YEARS AGO. AND THEY BOTH HAVE BEEN SITTING THERE SINCE. IT SEEMS THE BIG TWISTED ROOTS UNDERWATER GREW AROUND AND TANGLED IT UP, SO IT'S THERE FOR GOOD. ANYWAY, WE TALKED WITH A MR. ESCARENO, AND HE FILLED US IN ON THE SITUATION. HE SAID IT'S ONLY THE ENGINE. HE'S CRAZIER THAN THE LAST GUY.

SO, BEFORE WE STARTED WORK THE NEXT MORNING, WE HAD THE REST OF THE DAY TO LOOK AROUND AND GET A FEEL OF THE PLACE. WELL, THE MEN DID. THEY WENT TO CHECK OUT THE DINOSAUR. ME, I GOT STARTED ON MY TAN. HUH, SOME TAN.

DAY 2-11

IT'S HOT!! LEMME OUTA HERE!! I HATE THIS PLACE ALREADY. WE HAVE TO DRINK BEER CONSTANTLY OR WE'LL DRY UP. THE CLIMATE IS SO STRANGE HERE, AND THE SMELL, IT'S DONE SOME WEIRD THINGS TO MY STOMACH. THE LIZARD, I THINK IS CALLED A BRACKINOSAURUS, OR SOMETHING LIKE THAT. IT'S ALREADY GETTING ON MY NERVES. BAD. THE NATIVES, THOUGH, USE IT AS A TEMPLE FOR PRAYING. AND DO THEY HAVE GREAT PARTIES AFTER MASS! I JUST LOVE THEIR MUSIC. IT'S A CROSS BETWEEN MARIACHI AND CORRACOBAN MUSIC. HARD TO BELIEVE, HAM? BUT, NOW IF IT SOUNDS LIKE I'M HAVING A BALL, I'M NOT. ALL WE DO ALL DAY LONG IS WORK, PLAN, GET INSTRUCTIONS, AND WORK. I HATE IT.

I FINALLY FOUND OUT WHY THIS JOB IS SO HUSH-HUSH. THIS SHIP WE'RE WORKING ON IS THE LEGENDARY SATURN STILLETTO. MANY YEARS AGO, DURING THE ZYMBODIAN REVOLUTION, IT WAS HIRED TO TRANSPORT THE BIGGEST LOAD OF PITO IN THE WORLD OUT OF ZHATO, BUT CAUGHT ITSELF IN A BATTLE AND WAS BLASTED. IT WAS LICKED...

BUT IT HAD ENOUGH SPARK LEFT TO FLY SO FAR INTO THE JUNGLE WHERE NO ONE WOULD EVER FIND IT. THE SHIP AND CREW WERE NEVER HEARD FROM AGAIN. MANY EXPEDITIONS WERE FORMED TO FIND IT BUT ALWAYS VANISHED IN THE JUNGLE. DUE TO WAR, THEY COULD NEVER SEARCH BY AIR. WHAT IT BOILS DOWN TO IS, WE'RE HIRED TO FIX THE SHIP, SO THEY CAN FLY IT OUT AND RETRIEVE THE PITO. I THINK IT'S STUPID. BY PULLING OUT THE STILLETTO, IT COULD KILL THE LOCAL'S ONLY CONTACT TO THEIR MESSIAH. BUT I GUESS A LARGE DEAD HUNK OF JUNK IS FAR MORE IMPORTANT THAN A LIVING THING. DAMN, THE STUPID THING WILL NEVER FLY AGAIN. WE'RE WASTING OUR TIME. BUT, WHAT THE HELL, WE'RE GETTING PAID FOR IT. THE LOCALS CALL IT THE MOUTH OF HELL, BECAUSE THEY SAY MANY HAVE VENTURED INSIDE BUT NEVER RETURNED. KINDA SPOOKY.

I'LL BET YOU'RE WONDERING HOW I KNOW SO MUCH ABOUT THE NATIVES AND I DON'T EVEN UNDERSTAND THE LINGO. WELL, WE HAVE OUR VERY OWN GUIDE FROM ZHATO, A YOUNG GIRL CALLED TSE TSE. SHE'S ONE OF THE ONLY PEOPLE IN THE WORLD WHO SPEAKS BOTH OURS AND THESE PEOPLE'S LANGUAGES.

AFTER DAYS OF JUST WORKING, WE FINALLY GOT A DAY OFF AND WENT INTO ZHATO. I LOVE THIS TOWN. BUT, WE ALL GOT SO DRUNK, THE LAST I REMEMBER, I WAS DANCING AND THESE GEEKS KEPT PINCHING MY BUTT. THEN THEY WANTED ME TO GO WITH 'EM, BUT RACE BEAT THEM UP. SO I JUMPED OFF A TABLE INTO RACE'S ARMS AND ALMOST SWALLOWED HIS FACE BY KISSING HIM. THEN I THINK I PASSED OUT. GOD, I WAS PENNY CENTURY FOR A NIGHT. BUT, THE NEXT MORNING MY POOR HEAD FELT LIKE WORLD WAR THREE, AND I WAS SO EMBARRASSED ABOUT THE NIGHT BEFORE THAT I HID MY FACE FROM RACE THE WHOLE DAY.

DAY 12-15

IT RAINED LIKE CRAZY THE PAST FEW DAYS SO WE'VE HARDLY WORKED AT ALL. I BORE MYSELF WHILE THE MEN TALK JOB.

TODAY THEY SENT OVER A HORNY DOCTOR WHO GAVE US SHOTS SO WE WOULDN'T CATCH ANY OF THE JUNGLE DISEASES. OF COURSE HE GAVE THEM TO THE MEN ON THEIR ARMS, BUT TOLD ME IT'S BETTER FOR FEMALES TO GET IT YOU-KNOW-WHERE. AND LIKE A STUPID SHIT I FELL FOR IT, TILL HE STARTED DROOLING ALL OVER MY BUTT. THE BOYS THOUGHT IT WAS KIND OF CUTE. I HATE MEN. ANYWAY, THE RAIN STOPPED AND IT WAS BACK TO WORK. EVEN IF EVERYTHING IS NOW SOGGY, THE RAIN DID CLEAR UP A LOT OF THINGS. THE DINOSAUR HAS A RICH TAN AND THE SHIP IS A PRETTY PURPLE. IF YOU CAN'T SEE THESE COLORS, I SUGGEST YOU ADJUST YOUR TV SET. AND AS FAR AS THE WEATHER IS CONCERNED, IT'S HOTTER THAN EVER NOW. SO THE FASHION OVER HERE IS NOW LITTLE AS POSSIBLE.

BUT SERIOUSLY, FOLKS, I'LL NEVER FORGET THIS DAY AS LONG AS I LIVE. DUKE, YAX AND TSE TSE WENT INTO ZHATO FOR SUPPLIES. RACE AND I WERE ALONE (HOLD IT, MAGGIE)...

MARGIE! WOULD YOU BRING THAT OVER HERE, PLEASE?

WATCH OUT! THE GROUND IS KIND OF SLIPPERY! DON'T... MARGIE!

WOW!

EEK! YOU CAN SEE RIGHT THROUGH ME! STOP LAUGHING! IT'S NOT FUNNY!

HEE HEE YA HA HAA... I'M SORRY! BUT IT LOOKED SO... HERE, GIVE ME YOUR HAND!

I FOUND THAT THIS MUD IS GREAT FOR MY SKIN. I'M GOING TO TRY TO BRING SOME WITH ME WHEN I FINALLY COME HOME. ANYWAY...

LOOK OUT!

IT WAS THE FUNNIEST THING I'D EVER SEEN. I DON'T KNOW WHAT MADE ME DO IT, BUT I'M KINDA GLAD I DID. IT WAS WONDERFUL.

WATCH OUT FOR THAT FIRST STEP! IT'S A LULU!

GLUG...

SO, YOU WANNA PLAY GAMES, HAH? OK! HERE WE GO, BABY!

NO! I QUIT! I GIVE! I...

I...

RACE WAS FINE, ONLY TOO WEAK TO GET UP. I SAT THERE AN HOUR HOLDING ON TO HIM. I DIDN'T WANT TO LET GO, BECAUSE I DIDN'T THINK I'D HAVE ANOTHER CHANCE. I MEAN, WAS HE MAKING A PASS EARLIER OR NOT? IT ALL WENT SO FAST. I GUESS I'LL NEVER KNOW, WILL I? STUPID SNAKE.

END OF PART I

34

DAY 16

DAMN IT! THINGS ARE GETTING WORSE HERE! IT'S GETTING HOTTER, WE HAVEN'T HAD A DAY OFF IN DAYS UPON DAYS, AND JUST BECAUSE WE'VE HAD A FEW CHANGES IN OUR JOB, AND RACE IS LAID UP FOR A COUPLE OF DAYS, DUKE MORALES HAS BEEN ON YAX'S AND MY ASS MORE THAN EVER NOW. SHIT! THAT'S ALL I NEED. WELL, ONE GOOD THING HAS COME OUT OF ALL THIS. I'VE ACTUALLY LOST, THAT'S RIGHT, LOST THREE WHOLE POUNDS!! I THOUGHT FOR SURE WITH ALL THAT BEER, I'D BE A BALLOON RIGHT NOW.

MECHANICSPART2MECHANICSPART2

JAIME 82

37

"WE WERE ALMOST TO THE END OF THE RIVER, WHEN MY CREW TURNED AGAINST ME! THEY WOULDN'T GO ANY FURTHER BECAUSE IT WAS TABOO (CHICKENS). SO WHEN I DEMANDED THAT THEY GO ON AHEAD, THEY WERE GONNA MAKE ME WALK THE PLANK! BUT THAT WAS POSTPONED..."

"I THINK THE CREW WERE BEING EATEN WHILE I MADE IT TO DRY LAND, BUT I DIDN'T CARE TO LOOK BACK! I JUST KEPT RUNNING. I ATE AND SLEPT IN THE TREES WITH THE MONKEYS AT NIGHT, AND RAN ALL DAY. I RAN TILL SOON THERE WAS NO MORE DAYLIGHT!"

"AND, FINALLY WHEN I COULD RUN NO MORE, I CAME ACROSS A CLEARING, AND THERE LAY SOME OLD MAN BONES WITH A MAP TO THE TREASURE AND A MACHETE! TALK ABOUT PERFECT! SO, NOW IT WAS THOSE JUNGLE BEASTIES WHO HAD TO RUN FOR THE HILLS! THEN I CHOPPED MY WAY TO WHERE I AM NOW!"

AND NOW I FIND YOU HERE ON SOME KIND OF JOB AND EVERYTHING! IT'S WONDERFUL!

HMM... I GUESS I SHOULDN'T BE TOO SURPRISED TO SEE YOU! YOU'VE ALWAYS HAD A KNACK FOR GETTING AROUND!

SO, TELL ME, WHAT ARE THE LOCALS LIKE HERE?

WILD! THESE PEOPLE ARE NUTS! THEY'RE ALWAYS HAVING PARTIES, DANCES, AND STUFF LIKE THAT! AND THEY'RE ALSO HEAVY INTO MAGIC! THEY'RE ALWAYS CONJURING UP LIGHT SHOWS AND STUFF! WILD, HUH?

MAGIC, HUH? YOU MEAN LIKE, THE KIND THAT CAN GIVE SOME-ONE SUPER POWERS ???

HERE COMES ME, ROCKET'S GIRL!

UM, GEE... I DUNNO! I NEVER THOUGHT OF THAT! HEY, PENNY...?

WHAT DO YOU THINK OF THE BIG MONSTER THAT GUARDS THE FORBIDDEN TREASURE NOW?

HAH! HE'S NOT SO TOUGH! WE'LL SHOW 'IM WHO'S TOUGH!

THINGS ARE GONNA GET FUN AROUND HERE, NOW THAT PENNY'S ARRIVED. NO MORE BORING WORK DAYS, JUST FUN, FUN, FUN! AND THE BEST PART OF ALL IS, SHE CAN'T STAND THE SIGHT OF RACE. ANYWAY, I WISH YOU WERE HERE. IT SURE IS A BREAK FROM CIVILIAN LIFE. NOT A PROBLEM IN THE WORLD.

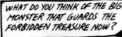

EAST SIDE BAD GIRLS

DAY 18-19 →

THIS IS A PICTURE OF THE FINALISTS OF THE MISS BIG BRA CONTEST. GUESS WHO WON? PENNY AND I WERE THE FINALISTS BECAUSE WE WERE THE ONLY CONTESTANTS. NONE OF THE LOCAL WOMEN WANTED TO ENTER BECAUSE THEY WERE SCARED. I JUST THINK THEY WERE AFRAID OF BEATING US (HA HA). FOR DAYS, WORK HAS BEEN REALLY SLOW SO I'VE BEEN DRUNK OFF MY ASS THE WHOLE TIME, SCREWING AROUND WITH PENNY AND THE LOCALS, TRYING TO GET SOMETHING GOOD OUT OF THIS TRIP. RACE HAS BEEN REALLY QUIET LATELY. PENNY BROKE THE POOR BOY'S HEART AWHILE BACK. HM, SERVES HIM RIGHT. BY THE WAY, THE MAN HOLDING US UP IS NOT A ROBBER, BUT BEN RUBEN, THE VILLAGE WRESTLER.

AND SPEAKING OF WRESTLING, IN A COUPLE OF DAYS WE'RE EXPECTING A COUPLE OF PEOPLE TO JOIN US FOR AWHILE, AND GUESS WHO ONE OF THEM IS? NONE OTHER THAN QUEEN RENA TITAÑON! YOU KNOW, THE WORLD PRO WRESTLING CHAMPION, FROM WHOM MY AUNT VICKI STOLE THE TITLE. RENA WOULD STILL BE CHAMP IF MY TÍA WOULD HAVE WRESTLED SCIENTIFICALLY (SHE USED THE ROPES). SMALL WORLD, HAH? AND DID YOU KNOW THAT WHEN SHE WASN'T IN THE RING SHE WAS TROTTING THE GLOBE FIGHTING MONSTERS AND CROOKS, STARTING REVOLUTIONS AND ALL OTHER TYPES OF HEROICS? AND TO THINK SHE PICKED THIS HOLE FOR HER NEXT SHINDIG. THIS WOMAN I'VE GOT TO MEET.

RENA'S HERE TO FIND OUT HOW DINOSAURS HAVE KEPT ALIVE HERE FOR SO MANY YEARS, AND WHY ONES FROM DIFFERENT TIME PERIODS COEXIST. I SAY IT'S BECAUSE THEY WERE WRONG ALL ALONG AND THAT DINOSAURS NEVER BECAME EXTINCT. THEY JUST GOT TIRED OF WORKING EIGHT HOUR SHIFTS AND MOVED TO THE WILD TO LIVE OFF THE LAND LIKE FLEABAG HIPPIES.

WELL, HOPITA, IT LOOKS LIKE IT'S GONNA BE A LONG TIME BEFORE I'LL BE SEEING GOOD OL' HOPPERS THIRTEEN AGAIN. OUR EMPLOYER IS NUTS!! HE MUST TRULY BE THE MONSTER FROM THE PADDED CELL. HE'S GOT US NOW TAKING THE WHOLE DAMN SHIP APART. THIS JOB JUST MIGHT FINISH US BEFORE WE FINISH IT. THERE'S SOMETHING FISHY GOING ON.

11

DAY 20

TODAY I WOKE UP WITH THE FEELING OF IMPENDING DOOM. I CAN ALWAYS TELL WHEN SOMETHING'S GOING TO GO WRONG, BECAUSE I WAKE UP WITH ALL MY COVERS ON THE FLOOR. SO, FOR THE WHOLE DAY I WAS EXTRA CAUTIOUS, AND IT GOT SO BAD THAT I SOON BECAME AFRAID OF MY OWN SHADOW.

WHAT'S UP, MAGGIE?

AAA

CHECK 'IM OUT! HE FOLLOWED ME HOME! I'M CALLING HIM GUILLERMO DEL JUEVIN!

Y-YOU'RE NOT SUPPOSED TO... MINGLE WITH LIZARDS HERE! T-THOSE ARE THE RULES HERE! IF THEY CATCH YOU...

CHEE, MAGGOT! WHY DO I MAKE YOU SO NERVOUS? DON'T WORRY, THIS GUY'S NO MEAT EATER!

WHAT YOU NEED IS A LONG VACATION AWAY FROM ALL THESE STUPID MACHINES! THEY'RE MAKING YOU A NERVOUS WRECK!

I'M SORRY! THIS JOB IS JUST DRIVING ME NUTS! WE'RE ALWAYS GETTING WEIRD INSTRUCTIONS, EVERYBODY'S UPTIGHT, AND NO ONE WILL TELL ME WHO WE'RE WORKING FOR! IT'S KINDA SPOOKY, Y'KNOW?

SANCHO SAN JO GAVE US THE SLIP AGAIN! HE'S WISE TO US!

¡SI!

END OF PART II

MECHANICS PART 3

JAIME 82

DAY 21 TODAY PENNY'S PET WAS DISCOVERED AND CAPTURED BY THE LOCALS. I DON'T DARE TELL PENNY HE'S BEING SAVED FOR THANKSGIVING, IT WOULD BREAK HER HEART. ANYWAY, OUR NEW VISITORS HAVE FINALLY SETTLED DOWN. FIRST, THERE'S PEDERO RODRIGUEZ SAN JO. HE'S THE SON OF OUR EMPLOYER. WHICH MEANS WE'RE WORKING FOR NONE OTHER THAN SANCHO CONRADO SAN JO! THE MAN WHO IS SO RICH, THE WHOLE ZYMBODIAN GOVERNMENT IS UNDER HIS FOOT. THE MAN WHO HAS PUT ZHATO, ZYMBODIA THROUGH SO MANY REVOLUTIONS, ASSASSINATIONS, ETC... THESE PAST FORTY YEARS, ALL BECAUSE HE THINKS ZHATO IS THE FUNNEST CITY IN ALL ZYMBODIA. HIS SON IS HERE JUST TO CHECK OUT DADDY'S PROGRESS. AND TALK ABOUT HORNY GOONS... YEESH...

THE FIRST DAY HE GOT HERE, HE CORNERED ME WHILE I WAS WASHING CLOTHES AND STARTED FEEDING ME THE OLD "WOULDN'T-YOU-RATHER-BE-WITH-ME-AT-A-DISCO" LINES. THEN HE STARTED GETTING DIRTY, SO I THREW SOAP IN HIS FACE (I KNOW, ♪ CHIVA RIVA RI, A PUN PUN PUN ♪). I'M PRETTY SURE HE GOT THE MESSAGE, BECAUSE NOW HE ONLY MAKES GOO GOO EYES AT ME. AND FINALLY, THERE'S BIG OL' RENA TITAÑON. ALL THE MEN GO GA GA OVER HER. WELL, SHE IS ATTRACTIVE, I GUESS, FOR AN ELDERLY WOMAN, THAT IS. ALTHOUGH, THERE'S ONE THING I'LL SAY FOR HER, SHE OUTDOES EVEN PENNY IN THE THINGS SHE'S DONE, THE PEOPLE SHE'S MET, AND THE PLACES SHE'S BEEN. BUT THE REAL TOPPING OFF THE CAKE IS THAT RENA WAS ONCE A SUPER HERO. AND AS YOU'VE PROBABLY ALREADY FIGURED OUT, PENNY CAN'T STAND THE SIGHT OF HER.

WHEN WE SHOWED OUR VISITORS THE SATURN STILLETTO, IT LOOKED AS IF RENA TITAÑON HAD SEEN A GHOST. WELL, SHE MAY AS WELL HAVE BECAUSE WOULDN'T YOU KNOW IT, IN THE OLD DAYS SHE USED TO TRAVEL IN IT DURING THE WESTSIDE WARS. IT SEEMS SHE HAD A LOVE AFFAIR WITH THE CAPTAIN OF THE SHIP. THEY PLANNED TO WED, BUT THAT WAS DAYS BEFORE THE SHIP WAS THOUGHT LOST. AND NOW EVERYBODY HERE IS DISCUSSING VENTURING DOWN INTO THE SHIP TO SEE IF THE CREW DIED WITH IT. WELL, I HOPE THEY CAN COUNT ME OUT, BECAUSE WHEN I WAS LITTLE, WE WERE PLAYING HIDE AND SEEK, AND THERE WAS THIS OLD REFRIGERATOR, AND WELL...

LATER TODAY SANCHO SAN JO SENT MS. TITAÑON SOME FLOWERS ON HER ARRIVAL. (THE MAN IS MAD ABOUT HER). IF HE'S ANYTHING LIKE HIS SON, THOSE ORCHIDS WERE BOOBY TRAPPED. I ASKED PEDERO WHY HE DOESN'T GO AFTER PENNY, AND HE SAID MY SHAPE WAS MORE HIS IDEA OF A WOMAN. I SHOULD BE FLATTERED, BUT I'M NOT. WAIT! I'LL HAVE TO WRITE YOU ABOUT IT LATER. RIGHT NOW, THE GHOUL HIMSELF IS PEEKING IN MY WINDOW. I WONDER IF THERE'S MORE AT HOME.

SAN JO MUST BE STOPPED! WE MUST INVADE ZHATO NOW! ¿BUENO?

¡BUENO!

⑭

DAY 22

TODAY IT WAS MINE AND RACE'S TURN TO GET SUPPLIES IN TOWN. RENA TITAÑON HAD TO COME ALONG TO TRANSLATE FOR US. Y'KNOW, I DIDN'T THINK TOO MUCH OF HER WHEN SHE FIRST ARRIVED, BUT NOW SHE'S MY HERO. MY GOD, SHE'S FANTABULOUS. I THINK I WAS JUST A BIT JEALOUS BECAUSE OF THE WAY EVERYBODY LOOKS UP TO HER. NOW I'M KINDA ASHAMED OF MYSELF. ANYWAY...WE WALKED INTO AN OLD AIRPLANE HANGER, AND THERE WAS AN OLD MAN SITTING BEHIND AN OLD DESK. AND WHEN HE SAW US COMING, HE STARTED TO BACK AWAY.

THIS GUY WAS HYSTERICAL! NEITHER RACE OR I COULD UNDERSTAND HIS LANGUAGE TOO WELL, BUT THE NAME "SAN JO" WAS PRETTY CLEAR...

NO!! GO AWAY!! I KNOW YOU'RE WORKING FOR SAN JO! WHY DON'T YOU PEOPLE LEAVE ME ALONE? BECAUSE OF YOU, MY WIFE HAS GONE CRAZY! AND MY KIDS...

CALM DOWN, OLD TIMER! WE HAVE ONLY COME FOR SUPPLIES!

NO! I KNOW WHAT YOU WANT! BUT YOU'RE NOT GOING TO GET IT!

HO'D IT, RUBEN!

THE SCUFFLE WAS OVER QUICKLY, AND WE GOT OUR SUPPLIES. AND AS WE WERE LEAVING, I COULD HEAR THE OLD MAN MUMBLING SOMETHING ABOUT NOT GETTING "IT". I WONDER IF HE WAS TALKING ABOUT THE PITO. THIS WHOLE SITUATION'S BECOME PRETTY SPOOKY.

ON THE WAY BACK RENA EXPLAINED TO US THAT THE LAND BELOW USED TO BE A VILLAGE THAT GREW COFFEE BEANS BEFORE IT WAS WIPED OUT BY MORTARS. SAN JO THOUGHT THEY WERE TOO MUCH COMPETITION FOR HIS PAN PIXLEY PEANUT COFFEE INVESTMENT.

AND A FEW MILES AWAY IN THE TOWN OF WINZENA, SAN JO CLOSED DOWN THE LARGEST FACTORY FOR MILES AROUND LEAVING THOUSANDS OF EMPLOYEES OUT OF WORK AND ALL NEWLYWEDS HOMELESS, ALL BECAUSE HIS NEW BROTHER-IN-LAW WHO WORKED IN THE FACTORY OWED HIM FIFTY DOLLARS. OH YES, HIS SISTER WAS STERILIZED (HIS ORDERS).

AND NOW WE'RE WORKING FOR THIS GHOUL. I DON'T MIND TELLING YOU, I'M ABSOLUTELY SCARED SHITLESS. SO WHEN WE WERE GETTING SUPPLIES, I STOLE A TV SET TO TAKE MY MIND OFF THIS JERK. BUT, WOULDN'T YOU KNOW IT, SAN JO OWNS ALL THE LOCAL NETWORKS, SO HE'S A HERO ON ALL CHANNELS.

CERRADO
GRACIAS, SI
COLORES, NO

THIS GUY CRACKS ME UP!

DAY 23·24

THIS CHICK'S BLOWING IT. I'VE BEEN DRINKING MYSELF SILLY THESE PAST COUPLE OF DAYS, AND I'VE BEEN FUCKING UP AT MY JOB. DUKE HAS ALMOST DECKED ME PLENTY OF TIMES, BUT I DON'T CARE. THIS IS SO RIDICULOUS!! EVERYBODY'S GOING AROUND AS IF NOTHING'S WRONG. THEY'RE ALL PRETENDING THEY DON'T KNOW ANY DAY NOW SAN JO WILL DROP AN H-BOMB ON US AND THEN HAVE HIS LUNCH. HIS SON EVEN KNOWS HE'S OFF HIS FLAMING ROCKER.

HEY, BITCH! DON'T WORRY! I'M NOT GONNA TOUCH YOU... THIS TIME! I JUST WANNA TELL YOU SOMETHING...

WHAT'S THAT?

YOU PEOPLE ARE ALL LOONIER THAN MY DAD IS! YOU PEOPLE ARE ALL STICKING AROUND, WAITING TO DIE! YOU ALL KNOW THIS IS GOING TO END IN TRAGEDY, ALWAYS DOES! DAD WILL FIGURE A WAY TO BLOW THIS THING SKY HIGH! YOU JUST WAIT...

THERE'S NOTHING HERE! THERE NEVER WAS! YOU'RE ALL JUST WASTING YOUR TIME HERE! YOU'RE ALL GOING TO DIE!

WHAT ABOUT YOU?

HA! DAD WOULD NEVER DO ANYTHING TO HURT ME! THE ONLY REASON YOU'RE ALL ALIVE RIGHT NOW IS BECAUSE I'M HERE! BUT THE DAY I LEAVE, KABLOOIE!

YOU'RE LYING...

MAYBE I AM, MAYBE I'M NOT! YOU KNOW, I KIND OF FEEL SORRY FOR YOU PEOPLE. I GUESS I'M JUST AS CRAZY AS DEAR OLD DAD! HA!

DICK!

HIS LAUGHTER WAS JUST AS SICKENING AS HIS OLD MAN IS. I HAD TO GET AWAY FROM THERE FAST, OR I'D THROW UP. THIS IS GETTING OUT OF HAND.

THE NEXT MORNING I WOKE UP WITH A BIG, BIG, BIG HANGOVER WONDERING IF PEDERO WAS BULLSHITTING ME. DUKE WAS ON MY BACK AGAIN, YELLING MY HEAD OFF AS I PRAYED TO THE PORCELAIN GOD. POOR ME.

I COULDN'T TAKE ANY MORE. I NEEDED STRENGTH. SO THAT NIGHT I LOOKED FOR PENNY. SHE'S ONE PERSON I COULD USUALLY TURN TO FOR ASSURANCE. BUT WHEN I FOUND HER, IT WASN'T THE SAME. THE NATIVES HAD HER PET FOR TONIGHT'S SUPPER. UGH.

UMM... SORRY, MAG... BUT I CAN'T ... YOU SEE...

PENNY'S OUT OF IT AND EVERYBODY ELSE IS TOO BUSY TO KNOW WHAT THE HELL IS REALLY GOING ON. SO, IT'S UP TO ME TO GET US OUT OF THIS. NOW, INSTEAD OF BEING SCARED, I'M GONNA GET MAD! I'M GONNA GET THINGS DONE! THIS GHOUL IS NOT GONNA GET AWAY WITH MURDER! I'M GONNA... I'M GONNA GET ANOTHER BEER AND SLEEP IT OFF AND GO TO WORK IN THE MORNING...

DAY 25

TODAY IS THE DAY I TAKE SHIT FROM NO ONE. NOT FROM SAN JO, HIS SON, DUKE MORALES, OR EVEN THAT DAMN DINOSAUR THAT KEEPS ME UP ALL NIGHT HUMMING AT THE MOON. EVEN RACE, WHO, EVER SINCE PENNY AND RENA SHOWED UP, WON'T GIVE ME A SECOND GLANCE. JUST LET THEM TRY TO GET IN MY WAY. I'LL SHOW 'EM. YAX IS OK, BUT HE DOESN'T SAY MUCH. AND TSE TSE SPENDS MOST OF HER TIME COOKING AND WASHING CLOTHES. NOW THAT ONLY LEAVES PENNY, WHO JUST TODAY DECIDED TO SPLIT THIS JIVE-ASS SCENE.

BUT, PENNY! YOU DON'T HAVE TO LEAVE! YOU'RE PRACTICALLY LOCAL!

WE ALL GOTTA GO SOMETIME, ¿QUE NO? I GUESS I'M GONNA JUST HEAD BACK TO ZHATO!

MARGIE! COME ON! WE GOTTA TALK JOB TODAY!

FINALLY GOT HERE, EH, LITTLE GIRL? HOKAY, FOLKS, I JUST RECIEVED NEW INSTRUCTIONS FROM OUR FEARLESS EMPLOYER, MR. SAN JO!

LAY 'EM ON US, BIG DADDY!

WE HAVE TO DROP EVERYTHING WE'VE DONE UP TO THIS POINT AND START CONCENTRATING ON FINDING A WAY TO GET DOWN TO THE BACK END OF THE SHIP! SAN JO FEELS WE'RE WASTING OUR TIME BY JUST...

SO WHAT ELSE IS NEW, DADDIO? I KNEW THIS WAS A WASTE OF TIME TO BEGIN WITH! ≈ BURP ≈

OH, REALLY?! SINCE WHEN DO YOU HAVE ANYTHING TO SAY ABOUT ANYTHING WE'RE DOING HERE?

SINCE NOW, DICK!

WHAT?! I HEARD THAT! YOU'RE DRUNK!

SO WHAT? I CAN STILL WHIP YOUR FUCKIN' ASS!

OH YEAH? WELL...

HEY, DUKE...

DUKEY, DUKEY... RELAX...

YOU KNOW I WAS ONLY TEASING YOU... YOU SHOULDN'T GET SO EXCITED... YOU'LL GET AN ULCER...

WELL... HARUMPH...

MEDIX

WHAT'S SO FUNNY?!

WAS I LAUGHING?

MEDIX

WAAAAAAAHH! I HATE HIM! I HATE HIM! I-I-I HATE HIM!

WAAA AAAAA

THERE, THERE, MARGARET! IT'S OK! NOW ST-·. OH, OH!

I'VE FINALLY BECOME GOOD FRIENDS WITH RENA TITAÑON. SHE HELPED ME WASH OUT HER BLOUSE AFTER I THREW UP ALL OVER IT. I WAS PRETTY DRUNK, I GUESS. WELL, AT LEAST DUKE GOT THE MESSAGE.

⑰

45

MECHANICS PART 4

DAY 27-29

LATELY I'VE BEEN HAVING THESE AWFUL DREAMS ABOUT THE STILLETTO. THEY STARTED WHEN WE GOT ORDERS TO VENTURE INSIDE TO THE BACK OF THE SHIP.

LAST NIGHT OUTSIDE MY HUT I HEARD DUKE AND RENA TALKING ABOUT THE STILLETTO WHEN IT FLEW, AND ABOUT ITS PILOT, HER ONCE SOON TO BE HUSBAND, BERNIE CARBO.

MANY YEARS AGO CARBO NEEDED MECHANICAL HELP FOR HIS NEW ROCKET SHIP AND DUKE GOT THE JOB. THEY BECAME GOOD FRIENDS FOR THE YEARS TO FOLLOW. THEN ONE DAY, DUKE INTRODUCED CARBO TO A FRIEND OF HIS NAMED RENA. IT WAS LOVE AT FIRST SIGHT.

SOON THE THREE OF THEM BECAME KIND OF A TEAM, BUT DUKE SOON DROPPED OUT BECAUSE HE FIGURED THREE WAS A CROWD. POOR DUKE, I THINK HE LOVED HER, TOO. ANYWAY, BEING DRUNK AND REMEMBERING OLD TIMES GOT DUKE ALL CHOKED UP, SO HE EVEN APOLOGIZED TO ME FOR ALWAYS GIVING ME A HARD TIME. THAT WAS NICE, BUT I'M STILL BUGGED ABOUT THAT SHIP. I DON'T THINK SAN JO IS MY ONLY WORRY ANY MORE. MAYBE I'M PSYCHIC.

THE NEXT DAY TSE TSE CAME RUNNING WITH SOMETHING IN HER HAND. IT WAS THE LATEST COPY OF THE DAILY PANADERÓN, A ZHATO NEWSPAPER. AT LAST I'D FIND OUT WHAT THE OUTSIDE WORLD WAS UP TO. IT WAS FULL OF FUN AND FASCINATING FACTS.

WHAT DOES S-A-N-J-O SPELL?

FOR INSTANCE, IT SAYS THAT RECENTLY ALL THE PEOPLE IN THE TOWN OF JINTÍN GAVE SAN JO A VERY WARM RECEPTION WHEN HE STAYED AT THE MAYOR'S HOUSE. BUT THEN SAN JO OWNS ALL THE NEWSPAPERS IN THE COUNTRY. I WONDER WHAT REALLY HAPPENED. I WONDER WHAT THE PEOPLE OF ZYMBODIA REALLY THINK OF SANCHO CONRADO SAN JO.

DID THEY GET HIM?

NO! HE HAD A TRAP DOOR!

47

DAY 30

SOMETHING FISHY IS GOING ON AGAIN. RENA TITAÑON HAS BEEN HERE TEN DAYS AND SHE HASN'T HAD ANYTHING TO DO WITH LIZARDS. AND MOST OF THE TIME SHE'S OFF IN ZHATO DOING WHO KNOW'S WHAT. ANYWAY, TODAY EVERYBODY WENT INTO TOWN BUT ME, RACE AND OL' HORNDOG. Y'SEE, I'VE BEEN LETTING PEDERO GET AWAY WITH A LOT. LIKE, NOT RATTING ON HIM WHEN I SHOULD, JUST SO HE WON'T GET DADDY ON US. WELL, TODAY WAS THEEEE STRAW THAT BROKE THE DINOSAUR'S BACK.

48

SEE? LISTEN! HE'S CRYING! HE'S OK!

WHAT IF HE SLIPS DOWN FURTHER? WE HAVE TO SAVE HIM!

I WAS AFRAID YOU'D SAY THAT!

WELL, IT HAPPENED. THAT GEEK WON'T GRAB MY BUNS AGAIN. HE BROKE HIS PINCHING ARM. ANYWAY, THIS IS IT, HOPEY. HERE'S WHERE I FIND OUT IF WE'RE TO BE WIPED OFF THE MAP, OR IF SANCHO SAN JO REALLY WANTS TO SAVE THAT PITO. I JUST WANNA GO HOME. NOW!

RACE, I KNOW HE DESERVED IT AND EVERYTHING, BUT THIS MAY GET US INTO A LOT OF TROUBLE!

I KNOW, BUT LISTEN! WHEN I WAS DOWN THERE...

I RETIRED TO MY HUT WITH THAT NAUSEATING FEELING OF IMPENDING DOOM. I DON'T KNOW WHAT I WAS GOING TO DO. SO I SAT STARING AT THE WALL. THEN CAME A KNOCK ON MY WALL.

RACE! WHAT...?

MARGIE! I CAN TELL THERE'S SOMETHING ABOUT THIS PROJECT THAT BUGS YOU! CAN WE TALK?

WELL, LATELY, I HAVE BEEN HEARING ALL THESE STORIES ABOUT MISTER SAN JO BEING THIS LUNATIC AND THAT US BEING HERE IS A BIG, BIG JOKE! THAT THERE REALLY IS NO REASON FOR US TO BE HERE! THAT...

WELL, YOU'RE RIGHT ABOUT THAT. WHEN I WAS DOWN THERE SAVING HIS SON, I FOUND A LARGE HOLE AT THE BOTTOM OF THE SHIP! AND...

THE WHOLE PLACE WAS FLOODED! AND WE ALL KNOW WATER DISSOLVES PITO! SO, THIS JOB IS OVER! YOU CAN START PACKING YOUR THINGS, WE'RE GOING HOME. YOU DON'T HAVE TO WORRY ANYMORE. EVERYTHING WILL BE OK FROM NOW ON...

IT STARTED GETTING DARK ALL AROUND US. AT FIRST I THOUGHT THE SUN WAS GOING DOWN. IT GOT DARKER... AND DARKER...

DUH... UMM, GEE! DAYS GO BY S-SO FAST HERE, DON'T THEY?

HUH? YOU OK? YOU'RE SHAKING LIKE A LEAF! MARGIE...?

AND THEN RACE STARTED FADING WITH EVERYTHING ELSE. I GUESS I WAS PASSING OUT. DAMN IT, SOMEBODY UP THERE MUST HATE ME.

...MARGIE? WHAT'S WRONG?

MARGIE?

MARGIE?

MARGIEEEE.......

BUT THEN I STARTED COMING OUT OF IT REALLY FAST. BUT RACE WASN'T THERE ANYMORE. ONLY THE FUNNY MASKS HANGING IN MY HUT. CUCUY...

AND THEN I REALIZE THAT I'M IN BED WITH ALL THE WINDOWS COVERED, I'M DRIPPING WITH SWEAT BECAUSE I HAVE A THOUSAND DEGREE TEMPERATURE, MY HUT SMELLS LIKE RUBBING ALCOHOL, AND THERE ARE SERIOUS MEN OUTSIDE DISCUSSING SERIOUS MATTERS. MY CONCLUSION IS THAT I ATE SOMETHING THAT DIDN'T AGREE WITH ME.

TSE TSE! HAVE YOU FOUND OUT WHAT IT IS MARGIE HAS?

YES SIR, MISTER RACE! SHE GOT MOE TOWNE FEVER! I THINK SHE GOT IT FROM A PLANT!

THAT'S EXACTLY WHAT IT WAS! THE OTHER DAY A FLOWER HAD EXPLODED IN MY FACE, BUT I DIDN'T THINK IT WAS SERIOUS, EVEN THOUGH I GOT SOME SHIT IN MY EYES.

IS IT VERY SERIOUS? I MEAN... COULD IT BE FATAL?

I'M SORRY, DUKE, BUT ALL I CAN TELL YOU NOW IS SHE'S TO REMAIN IN THAT HUT TILL THE FEVER IS BROKEN! AND THAT COULD MEAN THREE TO FOUR DAYS! ALL WE CAN DO NOW IS WAIT! ONLY TSE TSE AND I CAN GO NEAR HER SINCE WE'VE ALREADY HAD THE FEVER!

OH, GREAT! BECAUSE OF ME WE'LL PROBABLY ALL BE DEAD IN A FEW DAYS. WE COULD HAVE ALL BEEN SUN BATHING IN OXNARD VERY SOON. INSTEAD, WE'LL PROBABLY FRY ON A BIG, BIG ROCK IN THE ZHATO JUNGLE.

BECAUSE OF MY FEVER, MY AWFUL DREAMS OF THE SATURN STILLETTO HAVE TURNED INTO NIGHTMARES. THE DAMN THING JUST WON'T LEAVE ME ALONE. IT'S SPOOKY.

HA HA HA HA

SQUAD LEADER TO SADIE ONE, TWO, THREE, AND FOUR! NEXT STOP: ZHATO!

23

DAY 31-32

SORRY I HAVEN'T WRITTEN YOU IN A WHILE, BUT THE PAST WEEK HAS BEEN OFF THE DEEP END. MY FEVER RAN SO HIGH I COULDN'T LIFT MY ARMS, MY INSIDES FELT LIKE THEY WERE ON FIRE, MY SKIN FELT LIKE A MILLION NEEDLES WERE POKING INTO ME, MY EYES WERE ALMOST GONE, MY FINGERNAILS TURNED PURPLE AND I GREW THESE GROSS, GIGANTIC, GREEN FEVER BLISTERS ALL OVER MY FACE AND CHEST. I WAS A MESS. I COULD TELL I WAS FADING FAST, BUT TSE TSE AND RENA WOULD ALWAYS BE THERE TO LET ME KNOW I WAS STILL A-ROUND TO MEET THE SOON-TO-BE WRATH OF SAN JO.

I WAS SO DELIRIOUS THAT ALL I REMEMBER WAS A BIG, BIG SHADOW COME INTO MY HUT AND IT STARTED PAINTING THE WALLS. AND THEN IT STARTED TO SMELL LIKE OLD, MOLDY TORTILLAS. I THOUGHT FOR SURE I WAS BEING PICKED UP TO GO TO THE OL' BARRIO IN THE SKY.

JUST THEN, ALL THE THINGS IN THE ROOM STARTED SLAMMING LIKE CRAZY. I THOUGHT THAT WAS MY GOING AWAY PARTY. I SCREAMED.

THAT WAS WHEN I STARTED TO REALLY GET SCARED. EVERYTHING STARTED TO GET DULL, AND THEN CAME THE KOOKY PATTERNS, BUT THE THING TO TOP IT ALL OFF WAS THE MARCHING DOUGHNUTS.

IT SEEMED LIKE FOREVER, AND JUST WHEN I WAS READY TO CASH IT IN, I COULD HEAR A WOMAN CRYING. THEN ALL OF A SUDDEN I GOT REALLY COLD. AND THE CRY GOT LOUDER, AND I GOT COLDER. AND THE CLOSER THE CRYING GOT, THE COLDER I GOT.

END OF PART IV

MECHANICS PART 5

JAIME 82

DAY 33-36

WITH MY SICKNESS ALL GONE, I WOKE UP TODAY FEELING LIKE I COULD FLY. TSE TSE TOLD ME I SLEPT THREE WHOLE DAYS. SHE ALSO TOLD ME THAT IT WASN'T MOE TOWNE FEVER I HAD, IT WAS THE VAN SCOY FLU, WHICH IS WORSE. SHE SAID IT WAS A MIRACLE I LIVED THROUGH IT. MUST BE THE CHICANA BLOOD. ANYWAY, I WON'T BE SHOWING MY FACE TO ANYBODY TILL THESE UGLY MONSTER BUMPS GO AWAY. I TRULY LOOK LIKE A BEAST FROM THE HAUNTED DAIRY. HOW EMBARRASSING, HAH? EARLIER TODAY I HEARD THE MEN TALKING ABOUT THAT DAMN SHIP AGAIN. THEY WANT TO VENTURE INSIDE. THEY'LL BE SORRY IF THEY DO.

THE BOYS ARE IN ZHATO RIGHT NOW! THEY'RE...

OH, GOOD! BECAUSE I'VE GOT A VERY FUNNY FEELING ABOUT THAT SHIP...

WHEN I WAS RAGING WITH FEVER, I HAD THESE REALLY CRAZY DREAMS ABOUT ME GOING DOWN INTO THE SHIP ALL ALONE! AND THE FURTHER DOWN I WENT, THE MORE I GOT THIS STRANGE FEELING, AS IF SOMETHING ALIVE WAS DOWN THERE WAITING! OR EVEN THE SHIP ITSELF... LIKE IT WAS ALIVE, WAITING TO SWALLOW ME! YOU CAN FEEL IT, TOO! I KNOW YOU DO! YOU DO... DON'T YOU...?

WELL, YOU DON'T HAVE TO WORRY! NO ONE WILL BE GOING DOWN THERE! THE WHOLE JOB HAS BEEN CALLED OFF! SAN JO HAS HAD THE WHOLE PROJECT DROPPED! KAPUT!

THEN, WE CAN GO HOME NOW?

"NOT FOR AWHILE! THE BOYS ARE IN ZHATO BECAUSE RACE WAS ARRESTED FOR BEATING THE HELL OUT OF PEDERO RODRIGUEZ SAN JO! DUKE AND YAX WENT ALONG TO ACT AS HIS DEFENSE! I SHUDDER TO THINK HOW THAT TRIAL IS TURNING OUT! POOR RACE."

SHOULDN'T WE TAKE THE CHOPPER AND GET TO THEM RIGHT AWAY?

NO GOOD! WHEN SAN JO ENDED THE JOB, HE TOOK AWAY ALL HIS TOYS, TOO!

"HE TOOK AWAY EVERYTHING HE SUPPLIED YOU WITH! INCLUDING THE CHOPPER, FOOD, TOOLS, ETC... ALL THAT'S LEFT IS TSE TSE, YOU, ME AND THE LOCALS! THEY ALREADY AGREED TO SHARE THEIR FOOD WITH US IF WE HELP WITH THE CHORES. AT LEAST SAN JO HAD THE DECENCY TO LEAVE THESE POOR PEOPLE ALONE."

"WHILE YOU SLEPT THOSE PAST THREE DAYS, THAT SCREWBALL SAN JO HAD A NEWSTEAM FLOWN OVER TO COVER 'THE STORY OF THE YEAR!' BUT THAT ENDED WHEN THE GOOD OL' DINOSAUR ATE THE CAMERA."

SO YOU BETTER GET USED TO THIS PLACE, BECAUSE WE CAN'T LEAVE TILL RACE IS OUT OF THE CLINK! AND THAT'S GOING TO BE A LONG TIME! JUST US, THAT DINOSAUR, AND...

...AND THE MOUTH OF HELL...?

YEAH...

BERNIE... (SIGH)

26

DAY 37

ANOTHER DAY PASSED AND THE BOYS STILL HAVEN'T RETURNED, AND SAN JO HASN'T YET LOWERED THE BIG ONE ON US. ALL DAY LONG RENA AND TSE TSE WORK WITH THE NATIVES WHILE I LIE HERE WAITING TO LOOK LIKE A HUMAN BEING AGAIN.

MARGARET!!

WUZZAT? RENA?

MARGARET! COME HERE! HURRY!

RACE IS BACK?

HURRY, MARGARET! YOU'VE GOT TO SEE THIS!

I'LL HAVE TO COVER MY FACE! WOULDN'T WANNA SCARE ANYBODY!

WHAT IS IT, RENA? ARE THE BOYS BACK?

BETTER! THIS IS ONCE IN A LIFE-TIME! CHECK IT OUT!

WOW! WHAT ARE THEY DOING?

THEY CALL IT DRIFT YEAR! KIND OF LIKE FLYING SOUTH FOR THE WINTER! ONLY THIS HAPPENS ONCE EVERY TEN YEARS!

CHIWIS! THAT'S FANTA... WHAT'S WRONG?

TOROMBOLO!

WHAT'S WRONG? WHAT DID I SAY? PLEASE, TELL ME!

OH, FOR... TAKE IT OFF!

DAMN IT! NOW YOU DID IT! THIS IS THE MASK OF TOROMBOLO!

I HAD TO USE SOMETHING TO COVER MY FACE SO NO ONE WOULD SEE MY MONSTER BUMPS!

"TOROMBOLO IS THEIR GOD OF HOPE. THE LEGEND SAYS THAT A THOUSAND YEARS AGO, HE CAME DOWN TO RID THE LAND OF ALL BAD THINGS GOING ON, AND IF HE EVER HAD TO COME BACK, THEY WOULD SURELY PERISH. SO THEY THOUGHT YOU WERE HIM RETURNING TO WASTE THEM."

FLEE, MORTALS! FOR I AM TOROMBOLO!

I'M SORRY! I DIDN'T KNOW! NOW WE'RE THE ONLY ONES LEFT!

DON'T CRY, MARGARET! THEY'LL ALL COME BACK EVENTUALLY! A LITTLE TIRED MAYBE...

GEEZ! I THOUGHT YOU WAS POSSESSED!

55

DAY 38

STILL WAITING FOR THE BOYS TO RETURN, MY BLISTERS FINALLY DISAPPEARED AND I CAME OUT.

PLEASE, RENA? I'M DYING TO HEAR ALL ABOUT YOUR WRESTLING CAREER! AND THEN LIKE, WHAT HAPPENED AFTER...

WELL, OK! I USUALLY DON'T LIKE TO GET INTO IT, BUT SEEING YOU'RE A FAN OF THE SPORT...

"I WAS FOURTEEN AND SERVING IN THE P.P.S. JUNIOR HARD CORPS WHEN I STARTED TO ENJOY GOING TO THE MATCHES. MY FAVORITE WAS THE WOMEN'S CHAMPION, TIGER ROSA. I'D FOLLOW HER EVERYWHERE SHE'D GRAPPLE. SOON, I STARTED DREAMING ABOUT US AS TAG TEAM PARTNERS. THAT WAS WHEN I DECIDED TO ASK HER TO TRAIN ME.

"SHE AGREED, AND IN SIX MONTHS I BECAME A PRO! AND GIRL, WAS I HOT! I WON EVERY ONE OF MY MATCHES, AND WAS NAMED ROO-KIE OF THE YEAR. I WAS TEARING ALL THE OLD LOUD MOUTHS APART.

"BUT I SHOULD HAVE REALIZED IT WAS A SCAM WHEN TIGER FINALLY ASKED ME TO BE HER PARTNER. THE CON-TRACT'S FINE PRINT SAID I COULD ONLY WRESTLE ALONGSIDE HER. SO, FOR A FULL YEAR I WASTED MY TA-LENT STANDING BY AS TIGER TOOK ALL THE GLORY. SEE, BEING CHAMP, SHE HAD A LOT OF MONEY POWER. ENOUGH TO KEEP ME OUT OF THE SPOTLIGHT. SHE KNEW I WAS STAR MATERIAL, AND SHE ALSO KNEW I'D STEAL HER TITLE SOON ENOUGH. HER CONTRACT MADE SURE I WAS PUT ASIDE. BUT SOON, MY CONTRACT SOMEHOW GOT TERMINATED, AND I WAS READY TO DESTROY HER. BUT, AS ALWAYS, THERE WAS A CATCH.

"A NOBODY WASN'T ALLOWED TO SHOOT FOR THE WORLD TITLE! BUT THAT DIDN'T STOP ME, I HAD TO TAKE ON ALL THE BIGGIES BEFORE I COULD GET MY HANDS ON TIGER. FIRST, I MADE FORMER CHAMP, BAD MONTANA JANE EAT SHIT. THEN I BEAT THE STATE CHAMP, ANN AUSTIN. IT'S TOO BAD BECAUSE SHE WAS A GOOD FRIEND. FINALLY, I MADE THE NA-TIONAL CHAMPION, FAT, OLD MARIA BRAVO PLEAD FOR MERCY. GIRL, I WAS ON FIRE!

"SO FINALLY WHEN I GOT A CHANCE AT THE WORLD TITLE, ROSA NEVER KNEW WHAT HIT HER. IT TOOK A LONG TIME, BUT IT WAS WORTH IT. I WAS NOW QUEEN RENA OF THE LADY WRESTLERS. AND BEING CHAMP WAS FUN. CHALLENGERS CAME IN ALL FORMS. MY BIGGIES WERE AGAINST MAD MALA, SULTRY SIRENA, THE BLACK WIDOW, WHO I UNMASKED, AND KITTY KATZ, THE HOT NEW-COMER I WAS SUPPOSED TO WATCH OUT FOR. HELL, IT LASTED FIVE MINUTES. I WHIPPED 'EM ALL!

"I WAS INVINCIBLE! FOR TEN YEARS NOBODY COULD BEAT ME! VERY FEW EVEN CAME CLOSE. I WAS GETTING BORED...

28

"SO THEN I DECIDED TO DO TAG TEAMING AGAIN. MY PARTNER WAS A NEWCOMER NAMED VICKI GLORI. AND SURE ENOUGH, WE RIPPED AND QUICKLY BECAME THE NEW WORLD TAG TEAM CHAMPS.

"FOUR YEARS WE WERE UN-DEFEATED, UNTIL ONE NIGHT WHEN WE WRESTLED THE VICIOUS HOGG SISTERS. I WAS IN TROUBLE. BOTH THOSE FAT BITCHES WERE STOMPING THE SHIT OUT OF ME. I CRIED AND CRIED OUT FOR HELP FROM VICKI, BUT WHEN I LOOKED UP, I SAW HER STARING AT ME BACK-ING AWAY SHAKING HER HEAD LIKE A DAMN COWARD. AND AFTER I WAS PLASTERED, PINNED, AND LOST OUR BELTS TO THOSE ELEPHANTS, VICKI CAME BACK TO THE RING TO HELP ME UP. I PASTED HER A COUPLE AND FLUNG HER OUT OF THE RING. I'LL NEVER KNOW WHY SHE EVER DID THAT, BUT FROM THEN ON, WE'VE BEEN GREAT ENEMIES. SHE TRIED TO STEAL MY TITLE SEVERAL TIMES, AND SEVERAL TIMES SHE ALMOST DID, BUT NOT BY WRESTLING ALONE. SHE BEGAN TO USE ILLICIT MEANS TO PREVAIL. I MEAN, SHE WAS DIRTY. SHE KICKED, PUNCHED, GAUGED, CHOKED, PULLED HAIR, ANYTHING TO WIN. SHE BECAME MERCILESS.

"BUT, AS ALWAYS I CAME BACK AT THE END TO WHIP THE BUNS OFF HER. UNTIL ONE DAY..."

"THAT ONE DAY, TEN YEARS AGO IN NEW KEOPS. IT WAS THE VERY FIRST WRESTLING MATCH TELEVISED VIA SATELLITE. IT WAS SHOWN IN THIRTY DIFFERENT COUNTRIES AROUND THE WORLD. TARZAN GOVENDER CALLED IT, 'THE MATCH OF THE CENTURY.' IT WAS WILD..."

OH OH! VICKI HAS RENA IN REAL TROUBLE NOW!

SHE USED THE ROPES... SHE USED THE DAMN ROPES! SHE USED THE GOD DAMN FUCKING SHITTY ROPES!

8-BUT WASN'T THERE SOMETHING ABOUT A REMATCH? I DON'T CLEARLY REMEMBER, BUT THEY SAID THAT YOU NEVER CAME OUT OF YOUR DRESS-ING ROOM, AND THAT YOU SKIPPED TOWN BECAUSE YOU TURNED YELLOW!

"THEN THAT'S WHEN I MET CAPTAIN BERNIE CARBO! WE WERE GOING TO RULE THE WORLD TOGETHER IN HIS SATURN STILLETTO. BUT, WHEN HIS SHIP WAS LOST, I THOUGHT IT WAS ALL OVER. YOU KNOW, THERE'S NEVER BEEN ANYONE SINCE."

I REMEMBER THAT DAY, WHEN SHE FINALLY BEAT YOU! I SAW IT WHEN...

SAW IT?! HAH! WHERE?! HOW OLD WERE YOU?!

I SAW IT ON TV! I REMEMBER, IT WAS MY BIRTH-DAY! I HAD JUST TURNED EIGHT!

EIGHT?! YOU'RE BLIND WHEN YOU'RE A LITTLE KID! AND TV DIDN'T SHOW WHAT REALLY HAPPENED! I WAS CHEATED! SHE USED THE DAMN ROPES! I YELLED, "ROPES, ROPES!" BUT WE HAD A DEAF REF! SHE USED THE ROPES, I TELL YA!

ARE YOU KIDDING? I WAS KIDNAPPED FROM MY ROOM AND TAKEN TO WAR TORN ZYMBODIA! THEY LOVED MY WRESTLING SO MUCH THAT THE DICK DICTATORS OF DURIA PAN MADE ME QUEEN! I LATER TURNED ON THEM AND JOINED THE BLACK FIST LIBERATION ARMY! I WAS ITCHING TO GET BACK TO THE RING, BUT I WAS JUST TOO BUSY!

COME ON! LET'S GO GET SOME BEER!

PERVEZ SAYS: IT'S HERE! EVACUATE!

WAR COME SOON GET OUT! SPLIT!!

HELP!

57

DAY 39

THE DAYS ROLL ON AS WE SIT HERE WAITING FOR THE BOYS TO RETURN. TODAY IT RAINED LIKE CRAZY, BUT RENA WAS STILL OUT THERE LOOKING OVER THAT STUPID SHIP. I HOPE SHE DOESN'T GO NUTS LIKE EVERYBODY ELSE. THIS IS PROBABLY THE LAST LETTER YOU'LL GET FROM ME BEFORE I GET HOME (IF?). I'M LUCKY TO GET IT OUT BECAUSE SOME GUYS CAME TO SEE IF THERE WAS ANYTHING LEFT OF SAN JOS, AND ONE GUY FELT SORRY FOR US AND WAS NICE ENOUGH TO MAIL IT FOR ME. KINDA LOOKED LIKE FRANKENSTEIN.

CHIWIS, WHAT A NIGHT FOR THE OUIJA BOARD OR A SEANCE OR SOMETHING

YOU LIKE THE SPOOKY STORIES, MARGARET? WHY NOT LET'S TELL THE SPOOKY STORIES, YES?

WHERE I COME FROM, IN THE VILLAGE IS A GHOST THEY CALL THE DAMACHER! THAT MEAN "THE WALKING WIDOW." SOME CALL HER LA CUCUY!

NO, TSE TSE! I DON'T WANT TO TELL SPOOKY STORIES!

AND EVERY NIGHT SHE WALKS ON THE STREET LOOKING FOR HER BONES! AND SHE DRESS ALL IN BLACK...

TSE TSE! STOP! I GET TOO SCARED! PLEASE!

AND HER HAIR AND SKIN BE SNOW WHITE! AND HER HAIR GO ALL OVER THE PLACE! AND HER EYES GO POP POP OUT OF HER CHEEKS! AND...

TSE TSE! STOP!

HER TEETH ARE GREEN AND BIG LIKE A TIGER! AND HER FINGERS BE LONG AND RED! AND...

NNGH...

SHE GOES IN THE BAR AND SAY, "DID YOU SEE MY BONES?" AND THEY SAY, "NO!" THEN SHE GO KNOCK ON THE DOOR AND SAY, "DID YOU SEE MY BONES?" AND THEY SAY, "NO!" AND SHE CRY JUST LIKE A BABY OUTSIDE ALL NIGHT LONG... WAAAAAAHHH

AND SHE GO TO THE WINDOW AND SAY, "DID YOU SEE MY..."

THE WINDOW...?

SCREEEAM!

WHAT'S THE MATTER WITH YOU TWO? IT'S ONLY ME!

HEE HEE HEE HEE YA HAA HA HA HA HA HA HAAAAA

THAT NIGHT I DIDN'T WANT TO SLEEP ALONE.

WELL, TOMORROW RENA'S FINALLY GOING DOWN INTO THE SATURN STILLETTO TO CLEAR ALL OUR SUSPICIONS OF THE DAMN THING. WELL, TIME HAS RUN OUT FOR THIS LETTER. I HOPE I SEE YOU AGAIN, HOPEY.
LOVE YOU,
MAGGIE

END OF PART II

YOU KICK PEDERO'S ASS, EH? BOY, YOU REALLY GONNA BE FAMOUS NOW, EH? HAH! DON'T WORRY TOO MUCH, SAN JO GOT A HEART! MAYBE HE LET YOU FIX HIS VIBRATOR, EH? THEN HE LET YOU OFF IN SAY, TWENTY YEARS?

WONDERFUL! THEN MAYBE I CAN FIX THINGS IN THE OLD FOLK'S HOME WHEN I GET OUT!

YES, YAX! I KNOW! I KINDA SCREWED THINGS UP FOR RACE IN THERE, BUT WE GOTTA GET HIM OUT! SAN JO JUST MAY DO SOMETHING FOOLISH!

PSST... FOLLOW ME!

THAT'S RIGHT! I GOT IT RIGHT FROM (ULP) SAN JO HIMSELF! YES! PROJECT STILLETTO IS NO LONGER! PLAN NEIN IS NOW IN EFFECT!

I KNEW IT! I KNEW IT! RENA'S BEEN GONE TOO LONG, SO SHE'S NOT COMING BACK! T-THE STILLETTO SWALLOWED HER, TSE TSE! I TOLD HER NOT TO GO DOWN THERE! I TOLD HER...

STOP CRYING, MARGARET...

RENA TITAÑON HAS RETURNED! TA DAAA...

PLEASE EXCUSE THE DRAMATICS, GIRLS! THE OLD GRAY MARE, SHE AIN'T WHAT SHE USED TO BE!

DID YOU FIND A MONSTER? DID IT TRY TO EAT YOU UP GOOD?

HELL, (OUCH) THERE AIN'T NOTHING DOWN THERE! (OOCH, OUCH) THE SATURN STILLETTO IS JUST ONE DEAD PAIN IN THE ASS!

YOU MEAN...?

"OH, SURE, I FOUND A FEW THINGS! LIKE, I FOUND THAT RACE WAS RIGHT ABOUT ALL THE PITO DESTROYED BY THE SEA...

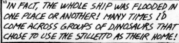

"IN FACT, THE WHOLE SHIP WAS FLOODED IN ONE PLACE OR ANOTHER! MANY TIMES I'D COME ACROSS GROUPS OF DINOSAURS THAT CHOSE TO USE THE STILLETTO AS THEIR HOME!

"I EVEN RAN INTO A FEW OLD FRIENDS, BUT NOWHERE IN THE SHIP COULD I FIND BERNIE CARBO'S BODY... FORTUNATELY...

"AT FIRST I ALMOST WANTED THAT SHIP TO SWALLOW ME UP. BUT, YOU KNOW, THE DEEPER I WENT DOWN INTO IT, THE MORE I GOT THE FEELING I WAS THE ONLY THREAT IN THE WHOLE DAMN THING. I SOON REALIZED I HAD ABSOLUTELY NOTHING TO FEAR..."

"THEN I KNEW IT WAS TIME TO LEAVE WHEN I ACCIDENTLY OPENED THE WRONG HATCH! WHATEVER WAS DOWN THERE IS NOW PART OF THE WORLD'S LARGEST AQUARIUM! HELL, THERE NEVER WAS ANY MONSTER DOWN THERE..."

BUMP BAM BOO

THERE'S YOUR DAMN MONSTER!

AIEEE!!

HE'S HERE! TOROMBOLO! NO! MARGARET! WHERE YOU GOING?!

I GOTS TO KNOW!

NO, MARGARET! IT'S TOROMBOLO! AND HE BE ANGRY AT US! WE'S HAS TO RUN, OR WE DIE!

OH MY GO— NO, IT'S NOT TOROMBOLO... IT'S...

IT'S WORSE! IT'S... IT'S... SAN JO!

...WELL, YOU COULD PRETEND YOU DROPPED YOUR KEYS RIGHT NEXT TO MY CELL!

SO YOU CAN ESCAPE? FEH!

ESCAPE? NOW, WHY WOULD I WANT TO...

¡ALTO!

KI KILIN...

OYE, KIKI... I MEAN LIKE, WHAT'S SHAKIN'?

AY KARAY...

62

64

DOWN IT WENT. DOWN IT ALL WENT. THE DINO-SAUR, THE PAIN IN THE ASS SATURN STILLETTO, ALL THOSE FEARS I HAD THAT PAST MONTH, ALL OF IT. IT WAS KINDA LIKE TURNING THE HANDLE AND FLUSHING THIS BIG, BIG TOILET KNOWN AS MY HEAD. I FELT SO RELIEVED. BUT IT WASN'T OVER YET.

WE FINALLY REACHED THE OUTSKIRTS OF ZHATO WHEN SOME SOLDIERS TOOK AWAY OUR CHOPPER AND WE HAD TO WALK. AFTER A WHILE WE REACHED THE TOWN ONLY TO FIND IT A FUCKING WRECK. PEOPLE WERE RUNNING ALL OVER THE PLACE LAUGHING, CRYING, LOOTING, DANCING, FIGHTING, WHATEVER THEY COULD THINK OF. I GUESS IT WAS WAR. PENNY DIDN'T CARE, RENA LOVED IT, AND I WAS SCARED OUT OF MY SHIT. IT WAS KIND OF EXCITING, THOUGH, WHEN WE SAW THEM BRING DOWN THE STATUE OF SAN JO THEY HAD IN A PARK.

MR. RACE! WE REGRET TO INFORM YOU THAT SANCHO SAN JO AND HIS ENTIRE FAMILY HAVE FLED THE COUNTRY AND ARE NOWHERE TO BE FOUND. HE TOOK WITH HIM HIS PRIVATE DOCUMENTS, SO ACCORDING TO LAW, YOU AND YOUR COLLEAGUES CANNOT BE PAID UNTIL HE IS LOCATED. BUT, YOU'LL BE HAPPY TO HEAR YOUR SENTENCE HAS BEEN COMMUTED. SINCE WE CANNOT LOCATE THE PLAINTIFFS WE CANNOT HAVE A CASE! CONGRAD-ULATIONS, MR. RACE!

THANK YOU!

SO, ALL ALONG THE PEOPLE OF ZYMBODIA PLANNED TO DESTROY THEIR SELF APPOINTED LEADER. AND RENA, WHOM THEY CALL "LA TOÑA," WAS BEHIND THE WHOLE THING. WHAT A WOMAN. SHE SHOWS THE PEOPLE HOW TO THINK FREE THEN MOVES ON. WILD.

HO'D IT, RENA!

WE LEFT TSE TSE AT THE ORPHANAGE IN EL PICASON, WHERE SHE LIVES WITH TWENTY OTHER KIDS. I PROMISED TO GO BACK AND VISIT HER IF SHE TOLD ME HER REAL NAME. IT'S ROSA COLORES ARRIAGA BANUELOS. I PROMISED TSE TSE I'D WRITE HER.

73

75

76

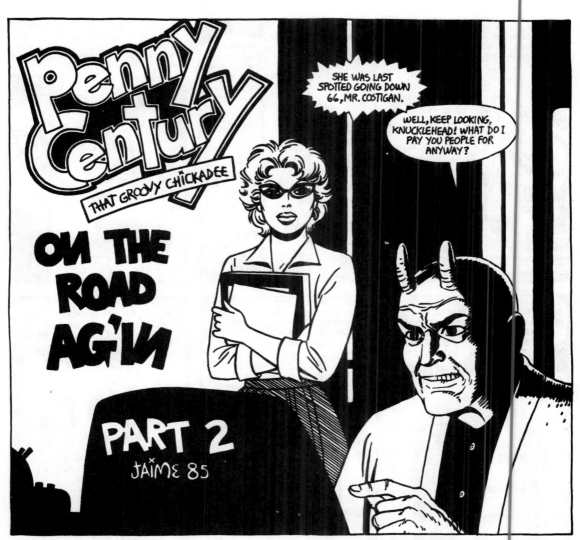

OH. IT'S THAT WOMAN CALLING AGAIN, SIR.

ARE YOU INSANE, BANCHINI? HANG UP, ALREADY!

⟨ANOTHER ONE CLAIMING TO BE HIS WIFE, EVA?⟩

⟨NOT THIS ONE, GRETA. THIS WOMAN ONCE SHOWED UP WITH ACTUAL EVIDENCE OF THEIR MARRIAGE. NATURALLY THE OLD MAN DENIED ALL AND HAD HER REMOVED FROM THE PREMISES.⟩

HATO

⟨OOH, WHEN I SEE HIM WITH THAT BLONDE SLUT I JUST GET SICK TO MY STOMACH. AND THAT POOR WOMAN IS TREATED LIKE...⟩

⟨FROM HER PHONE CALLS I GET THE IMPRESSION THIS WOMAN IS NOT ALL THERE.⟩

⟨WOULD YOU BE IF YOU WERE MARRIED TO THAT OLD FART? ONE OF THESE DAYS I'M GOING TO EXPOSE HIS LITTLE GAME, EVEN IF IT COSTS ME MY JOB.⟩

BOMBER, I THINK WE BETTER GO NOW.

NOT TILL YOU TELL ME HOW YOU KNEW THAT MAID AT THE MOTEL WAS ONE OF COSTIGAN'S SPIES.

OH, THAT'S EASY. I KNOW THE WAY COSTIGAN THINKS. IT'S A RIOT TRYING TO FIGURE OUT WHICH ONES ARE HIS BOYS.

YEAH? LET'S TRY THIS CROWD ON THE STREET. WHAT DO WE LOOK FOR?

OH, I DUNNO. HE'S USED INDIAN CHIEFS BEFORE... SHOE SHINE BOYS... SOME OF HIS SPIES ARE SO DUMB THEY GIVE THEMSELVES AWAY.

NO KIDDIN'?

BLIND

3

86

89

MECHANICS

93

94

MECHANICS PART TWO

DEAR HOPEY AND GANG,

ALOHA! OR AS THEY SAY HERE IN FUNNY, SUNNY, RIO FRIO... KAMANA-WANALEYA! MAN, THEY SURE DON'T WASTE TIME HERE, I TELL YA. ONCE YOU STEP OFF THE PLANE, ≥ CACHOING ≥ YOU'RE ENGAGED OR SOMETHING. BUT YOU DON'T HAVE TO WORRY ABOUT THIS ONE, JACK. I'VE GOT MY EYE ON SOMETHING A LITTLE CLOSER TO HOME, AND HIS INITIALS ARE RANDALL RACE. TELL PENNY I KNOW THAT HE'S JUST A MACHO CREEP AND I JUST LIKE HIM BECAUSE HE'S A PROSOLAR MECHANIC. WELL, MAYBE, MAYBE NOT. WE SHALL SOON SEE.

ANYWAY, THIS JOB WE'RE ON CALLS FOR ONLY TWO MECHANICS. A PRO MECH AND (KAFF KAFF) HIS ASSISTANT. THAT'S RIGHT, BOYS AND GIRLS. IT'S JUST RACE AND I LET LOOSE IN THIS STRANGE, STRANGE, EXOTIC LAND. OH, HOW WILL WE EVER MANAGE?

WELL, TO TELL YOU THE TRUTH I HAVEN'T REALLY SEEN MUCH OF THE STUD SINCE WE GOT HERE. HE'S BEEN OFF TALKING JOB (AS USUAL), SO I'VE JUST BEEN HANGING AROUND THE BEACH GETTING FAT LIKE ALL THE OTHER LAME TOURISTS. BUT, MY TIME SHALL COME, BABY.

LOVE YOU,
MAGGIE

CHEPAN! THE ISLE OF GREAT HISTORY! THOUSANDS OF YEARS AGO THE BLASCANS FLED TO THE ISLAND TO ESCAPE THE TYRANTS THAT RULED BLASCANIA (RIO FRIO). YOU KNOW, WITH ALL MY MONEY KEEPING THAT SINKING ISLAND AFLOAT, THOSE UNGRATEFULS STILL WANT ME DEAD. JUST WAIT TILL THAT BIG ONE COMES, BOY... AND WHEN THEY COME RUNNING TO ME...

YOU KNOW, I REALLY HATE TO BE PUSHY, BUT...

EXACTLY WHAT KIND OF WORK WILL WE BE DOING FOR YOU, DR. BEAKY?

ROBOTS, MY BOY! ROBOTS! A MILLION OF 'EM...

YEOW

SLAM!!

MARGIE! ARE YOU ALL RIGHT?

OH, MY...

WHOA... YEAH, I THINK SO.

WHAT HAPPENED? DID YOU SLIP, OR...

NO. IT FELT MORE LIKE I WAS THROWN.

CHINESS!

MUST I PUNISH YOU OVER AND OVER BEFORE YOU FINALLY UNDERSTAND? HM?

HM?

NO, DR. BEAKY, I'M ALL RIGHT! YOU DON'T HAVE TO...

A THOUSAND APOLOGIES, MISS CHAS-CARRILLO. I'LL MAKE SURE IT NEVER HAPPENS AGAIN. MY MAN ON THE ISLAND WILL FILL YOU IN ON THE DETAILS OF YOUR JOB. NOW, IF YOU'LL EXCUSE ME, IT'S TIME FOR MY MEDICINE. GOOD DAY.

WELL, MS. WINKS. YOU NOW HAVE PERMISSION BY DR. BEAKY TO ENTER CHEPAN.

THANK YOU. IS THERE A PHONE I CAN USE?

THERE'S ONE OUT IN THE HALL.

5

FRANCO? IT'S DOT. YEAH, I'M IN FRIO RIO AND... RIO FRIO, WHATEVER... AND I GOT PASSAGE TO THE ISLAND... YEAH, CHEPAN. THAT'S WHERE RACE IS WORKING. YEAH...

NO, SMART GUY, HE DOESN'T KNOW I'M HERE... YET. OH, GOTTA GO NOW, FRANCO. THERE'S A DOZEN GORGEOUS BLASCAN HUNKS BREATHING DOWN MY BACK JUST WAITING TO JUMP THIS BOD. UH HUH. WHO? RACE? NO WAY! OK, BYE BYE, SWEETIE.

THAT FRANCO'S GOT SOME KINDA IMAGINATION. ALL I WANT FROM RACE IS AN INTERVIEW, AND I'M GETTING IT, EVEN IF IT KILLS ME.

HEY, MARGIE! WASN'T THIS A GREAT IDEA RENTING THIS SMALL TUG TO TAKE TO THE ISLAND INSTEAD OF THE STANDARD LINER?

MAN, DO I FEEL GREAT!

GROWL!

YEAH. SWELL, RACE.

JEEP

STILL THINKING ABOUT THE INCIDENT IN DR. BEAKY'S OFFICE?

DOES HE ALWAYS TREAT HUMAN BEINGS LIKE ANIMALS? NOT THAT THAT SHOULD EVEN HAPPEN TO TEN DOGS...

AW, I KNOW BEAKY'S A SCREW BALL, BUT LET'S JUST FORGET ALL THAT RIGHT NOW. LOOK, WE HAVE ALL THIS NICENESS. NO NOISE... NO MACHINES... NO BOSSES... NO NOSEY REPORTER DOWN MY NECK...

WELL, THAT'S A STEP IN THE RIGHT DIRECTION.

OK, RACE...

HEY, BOSS!

JOE, I TOLD YOU NOT TO CALL ME BOSS! JUST CALL ME RACE!

OK, BOSS. BUT HERE COME THOSE COAST GUARDERS AN' THEY LOOK KINDA HUNGRY!

I'LL SLIP BELOW IF YOU DON'T MIND.

6

NO, DON'T GO! SINCE YOU'RE HERE, HOW ABOUT THAT INTERVIEW I'VE BEEN ASKING YOU SO NICELY FOR?

OH, CHRIST...

WHAT DO I HAVE TO DO TO GET IT THROUGH YOUR DINGY BLONDE HEAD THAT I DON'T WANT YOU NEAR ME? READ-MY-LIPS: I-DON'T-WANT-YOU-NEAR-ME! GET OUTA HERE!

SPLIT!

O-OK!

YOU ASSHOLE, FRANCO. YOU WERE RIGHT. COULD IT BE THAT I'M ACTUALLY FALLING IN LOVE? DOT, WHAT HAVE YOU DONE?

MAN, WHAT'S WRONG WITH ME? I'M COMING UNGLUED! I...

MARGIE!

MARGIE? YOU STILL HERE?

YEAH. I...UH...WAS JUST ABOUT TO GET TO WORK.

LOOK, MARGIE, I'M SORRY I ACTED THE WAY I DID. I JUST GET SICK OF ALL THIS BUSINESS BULL. I'M REALLY SORRY YOU WERE TRAPPED IN MY EXPLOSION.

THAT'S OK. I UNDER-STAND. THE PRESSURES AND ALL...

YOU DON'T KNOW HOW MUCH BETTER THAT MAKES ME FEEL. I JUST HOPE DOT WILL BE AS UNDERSTANDING AS YOU ARE. I BETTER FIND HER BEFORE ...

WHO?!

HELL, DON'T ASK ME!

END OF PART II

MECHANICS
PART THREE

SO FAR:
RACE AND MAGGIE ARE IN RIO FRIO HIRED TO FIX ROBOTS ON THE NEARBY ISLE OF CHEPAN AND REPORTER DOT WINKS HAS COME TO VISIT.

JAIME 84

YOU SAID THAT! WHY?

WHY WOULD I SAY THAT? MAGGIE'S NOT EVEN HERE!

I QUIT THIS FUCKING BAND, I SWEAR!

WHAT? AGAIN?

SHE'S WORKING WITH RAND RACE IN RIO FRIO, ISN'T SHE? HAS SHE WRITTEN YOU LATELY, HOPEY? HOPEY?

WHY IS HOPEY SO UPTIGHT?

IZZY ORTIZ HAD AN ACCIDENT AT HOPEY'S PLACE AND ALMOST DIED. SHE GAVE HOPEY QUITE A SCARE.

SO, AGAIN I'D LIKE TO APOLOGIZE FOR ALL THE TROUBLE I'VE CAUSED YOU, AND SO WE CAN BE FRIENDS I'M GOING TO FORGET ABOUT THIS INTERVIEW BUSINESS, OK?

I MEAN, WHO NEEDS A HUNDRED DOLLAR BONUS, ANYWAY? NOT ME, BOY!

AND WHO CARES ABOUT ALL THOSE MILLIONS OF FANS WHO CRAVE THE TRUE STORY OF RAND RACE'S LIFE AS AN EVER POPULAR PRO MECH?

TRYING TO MAKE ME FEEL LIKE A HEEL, DOT? IT'S WORKING.

HM, I DON'T MEAN TO. IT'S JUST THAT YOU'RE THROWING AWAY A LOT HERE. YOU KNOW, WITH MY COLUMN, I COULD MAKE YOU VERY FAMOUS. WITH YOUR LOOKS YOU COULD EASILY BECOME THE NEXT DEREK CI...

HELL, I HAVE A HARD ENOUGH TIME JUST KEEPING UP WORK! I HAVE BOSSES WHO KEEP WOMEN AS PETS, I HAVE ASSISTANTS WHO CLOBBER ME WITH ROBOT LIMBS...THEN DISAPPEAR!

BY THE WAY, WHERE IS YOUR LITTLE PARTNER THIS MORNING?

AW, SHE SAID SHE WAS ILL OR SOMETHING. YOU KNOW, BY THE LUMP ON MY HEAD, I'M BEGINNING TO BELIEVE SHE REALLY IS... MENTALLY!

3

THANKS FOR THE SWELL GET WELL GIFTS, GUYS. BUT YOU REALLY SHOULDN'T HAVE...

THAT'S OK, IZZY. I SEE YOU'RE RECOVERING NICELY.

YEAH, I FEEL GREAT! THOSE CHOCOLATE M&M'S YOU GOT ME REALLY DID THE TRICK.

YEAH. I FIGURED THE GREEN ONES WOULD HAVE MADE YOU SICKER.

WHERE'S YOUR LOUD ROOMMATE? HAVING MOUTH SURGERY?

OH, SHE DIED LAST NIGHT. IT WAS SAD BECAUSE SHE WAS ALREADY DEAD TEN MINUTES BEFORE ANY-BODY CAME TO CHECK ON HER. THE POOR WOMAN HAD AN INCURABLE VIRUS YOU CAN ONLY GET IN THE PALO PALO REGIONS. HAS SOMETHING TO DO WITH THEIR MULES, I DON'T KNOW...

ISN'T THAT AROUND WHERE MAGGIE IS WORKING?

⁝ ULP ⁝

WHAT'S WRONG, HOPEY? YOU SICK OR SOMETHING?

I GOTTA CALL MAGGIE.

PERHAPS MS. TITAÑON WOULD ENJOY ANOTHER FRUIT COCKTAIL?

NO, NO, THIS IS FINE, THANK YOU VERY MUCH.

RENA...

I DON'T KNOW WHAT TO DO. THE PEOPLE ON MY ISLAND ARE STARTING TO THREATEN ME NOW! I WANT TO AVOID ANY UNNECESSARY BLOODSHED. YOU KNOW...

MAYBE IF YOU COULD TALK TO THEM. THEN MAYBE...

LOOK, BEAKY. THEIR MIND IS ALREADY MADE UP. THEY WANT THEIR COUNTRY BACK FROM YOU AND THEY'LL STOP AT NOTHING TO GET IT.

BAH! I GIVE THOSE ISLANDERS EVERYTHING THEY NEED AND WHAT DOES IT GET ME? A BIG KNIFE IN MY BACK! WELL, WE SHALL SEE...

A FRIEND OF MINE TELLS ME YOU HAVE RAND RACE AND HIS ASSISTANT WORKING FOR YOU ON THE I... CHEPAN.

YES, BUT THEY HAVE NOTHING TO DO WITH THE MATTER AT HAND! I WANT YOU TO TELL THOSE ISLANDERS THAT...

I HAVEN'T SEEN MARGARET AND RACE SINCE ZHATO. MAYBE I'LL DROP IN ON THEM... WITH YOUR PERMISSION OF COURSE, DOCTOR BEAKY...

PHONE, DOCTOR...

YES, YES! GO ON! HELLO? WHO IS THIS?

THANK YOU. AND BEAKY, IT'S ONLY AN ISLAND FROM THE WATER. REMEMBER THAT, OR YOU'VE GOT MORE TROUBLE FROM THEM THAN YOU EXPECTED.

I'M SORRY, DOCTOR BEAKY, BUT THE REBELS ON CHEPAN HAVE INFORMED ME THAT IF YOU DON'T START NEGOTIATIONS WITH THEM CONCERNING THE ISLAND SOON, THEY'RE GOING TO HAVE TO..."RESORT TO DRASTIC MEASURES."

HAH?!

OH, THEY WILL, WILL THEY? WELL, YOU TELL THEM I'M CALLING THEIR BLUFF! THEY DON'T SCARE ME ONE BIT! LISTEN! I'M LAUGHING!

HA-HA-HA!

AT ONCE, DOCTOR.

CLICK!

THOSE BASTARDS ARE RUINING EVERYTHING! HOW EMBARRASSING. THEY ACTUALLY HATE ME. I CAN ONLY IMAGINE WHAT COSTIGAN IS GOING TO SAY. I'LL NEVER BE ABLE TO SHOW MY FACE AT ONE OF HIS SHINDIGS AGAIN. OH, WOE IS ME...

YOU KNOW, YOU'RE RIGHT? I THINK I'VE BEEN WORKING MYSELF TOO HARD. ALL THOSE MACHINES HAVE REALLY GOTTEN TO ME.

WHAT YOU NEED IS REST AND RELAXATION. AND I THINK I HAVE JUST THE THING FOR YOU...

6

YEAH, OK. BIG MAN. YEH... DID YOU DO IT TO PROVE SOMETHING, OR WHAT? LIKE, THAT YOU'RE STILL ALL MAN, OR JUST BECAUSE YOU PLAIN ENJOYED IT? DID YOU DO IT BECAUSE IT'S SO HARD FOR YOU TO EVEN ASK MARGIE TO PASS YOU A WRENCH? MAN, IF SHE FINDS OUT ABOUT THIS, ABOUT ME AND DOT... MARGIE REALLY LIKES YOU A LOT, YA BIG COWARD!

WAIT, WHAT AM I AFRAID OF? SO WHAT IF I GO TO BED WITH THIS WOMAN? I DON'T OWE MARGIE ANYTHING! SHE'S MY ASSISTANT MECHANIC, NOT MY GIRLFRIEND! SO WHAT IF SHE HAPPENS TO BE NICE... SWEET... SOFT... AND THINKS I'M THE GREATEST THING SINCE SEEDLESS WATERMELON.

WELL, I BETTER SIGN OFF NOW, HOPITA. HOW ARE YOU EVER GONNA PAY THIS PHONE BILL?

DON'T HAVE TO! DAFFY GOT A NEW CREDIT CARD NUMBER FROM HER DAD. THE OTHER DAY WE CALLED ZHATO AND TALKED TO THEIR NEWEST PRESIDENT.

WELL, IT WAS NICE OF YOU TO CALL, HOPEY. UH HUH. THANKS. I MISS YOU. BYE BYE.

NOW I FEEL LIKE A MILLION BUCKS! I DON'T EVEN MIND GOING UP TO RACE AND APOLOGIZING RIGHT TO HIS FACE! I JUST MIGHT HAVE TO GIVE A GREAT, BIG KISS TO THAT BUMP ON HIS HEAD. I THINK I SAW A LIGHT ON IN HIS ROOM.

SEE? I TOLD YOU THERE'S NOTHING TO WORRY ABOUT, ESPERANZITA.

I SUPPOSE YOU'RE RIGHT, PENNY.

REALLY? THEN WHAT ARE THE TEARS FOR MARGARET? I KNOW IT'S NOT BECAUSE YOU'RE SO EXCITED TO SEE ME. COME ON, YOU NEED A BIG SHOULDER TO CRY ON, HON?

HOPEY SURE LOOKS HAPPIER TODAY.

SHE TALKED TO MAGGIE ON THE PHONE FROM RIO FRIO LAST NIGHT. I GUESS ALL THOSE HINTS OF MAGGIE BEING DEAD WERE ALL COINCIDENCE.

I WONDER...

MISSILES OF OCTOBER

DOA

CALM DOWN, BEAKY! WHAT'RE YOU TRYING TO TELL ME?

THE ISLANDERS ARE DESTROYING MY FACTORIES AND WAREHOUSES IN CHE-PAN ONE BY ONE! WHO KNOWS WHAT THEY'LL TRY NEXT?

LATEST REPORT, DOCTOR BEAKY. THEY JUST BOMBED ANOTHER ON THE SOUTH COAST.

VERY WELL. I WANTED TO AVOID THIS, BUT THEY LEAVE ME NO ALTERNATIVE. GET ME GENERAL MATAPOLAS ON THE PHONE. WE'LL HAVE TO PLACE CHEPAN UNDER ARREST. HAS ANYONE BEEN HURT IN THE EXPLOSIONS?

NOT YET, SIR. THEY'VE ALL BEEN EMPTY OR CON-DEMNED BUILDINGS THUS FAR. IF YOU ASK ME, THEY ARE ONLY TRYING TO SCARE YOU.

BEAKY! MY ASSISTANT MAGGIE HAS GONE TO THE ROBOT WAREHOUSE.

OH, YES, AND RENA TITAÑON WAS GOING TO MEET YOU THERE ALSO.

RENA TITAÑON, TOO? WE'VE GOT TO WARN THEM BEFORE...

ALL COMMUNICATION HAS BEEN CUT OFF TO THE MAINLAND! I'LL SEND SOMEONE TO...

FORGET IT! I'LL GO!

YES, BOSS! I TOOK HER THERE MYSELF. SHE WAS ON HER WAY TO THE ROBOT WAREHOUSE YOU WORK AT. I DUNNO, I DON'T THINK IT'S TOO GOOD AN IDEA TO GO INTO CHEPAN RIGHT NOW. I SAW SOME BOMBS GOING OFF ON LAND.

YOU CAN TURN BACK AS SOON AS YOU DROP ME OFF ON LAND.

OH OH! IT'S THOSE RIO FRIO COAST GUARDERS AGAIN, BOSS, AND THEY LOOK MADDER THAN THE LAST TIME.

SHIT! STALL THEM FOR ME, WILL YOU?

117

118

ARE YOU SURE YOU SAW TWO WOMEN IN THE WAREHOUSE WHEN YOU PLANTED THE EXPLOSIVES?

I'M POSITIVE! ONE OF THEM CAME AFTER ME! I-I GOT SCARED...

...SO I RAN...

...BEFORE YOU COULD DEACTIVATE THE EXPLOSIVES. ARGHH! NOW BEAKY'S NOT ONLY AFTER OUR NECKS BUT OUR DICKS AS WELL!

YOU CAN SAY THAT AGAIN! HE HAS SOLDIERS BREATHING DOWN OUR NECKS! WE CAN'T STAY HERE MUCH LONGER.

DO YOU THINK THEY COULD HAVE GOTTEN OUT BEFORE...

I DON'T KNOW! I DIDN'T LOOK BACK, BUT I HEARD THE EXPLOSION...

WHERE WILL WE GO NOW?

WELL, WE CAN'T USE THE SEWERS. THEY HAVE BEEN SEALED OFF FOR YEARS NOW.

ARE YOU STILL THERE, RENA?

I'M STILL HERE.

WHY DO WE KEEP WALKING? I'M HUNGRY.

DON'T TALK. YOU'RE DELIRIOUS.

HOW LONG HAS IT BEEN?

OH, ABOUT TWENTY HOURS.

TWENTY HOURS? IT SEEMS MORE LIKE TWENTY DAYS!

MHMM. DON'T DRAG YOUR FEET.

MEANWHILE, OH, ABOUT TWENTY HOURS AGO...

③

HOOIEEE LO'D!

WHO'DA BELIEVED IT IN A MILLION YEARS THAT THIS OLD BOD COULD STILL MOVE FAST ENOUGH TO SAVE OUR NECKS! WE'RE MOSTLY LUCKY WE HAD THIS PIT TO DIVE INTO OR ELSE THAT BOMB WOULD'VE GOTTEN US BUT GOOD!

LOOKS LIKE THE WRECKAGE FROM THE BLAST SEALED OUR WAY OUT OF HERE. WE'LL NEVER BE ABLE TO CLEAR IT. TOO BAD. AS LONG AS WE'RE ALIVE, RIGHT, KID?

MY HEAD FEELS LIKE IT'S ON FIRE...

OH, IT'S NOTHING, REALLY. BLOOD MOSTLY. YOU'LL BE FINE. DO YOU HURT ANYWHERE ELSE, MARGARET?

NO, BUT EVERYTHING'S GETTING DARKER BY THE MINUTE. I THINK I'M GOING BLIND, RENA.

NO, THAT'S JUST THE FIRES GOING OUT. WE'RE GOING TO HAVE TO FIND SOME OTHER FORM OF LIGHT. I DON'T THINK FIRE WILL LAST TOO WELL IN THIS THIN AIR.

WELL, IF THERE'S A MINER AMONG THIS SCRAP OF ROBOTS WE MIGHT HAVE SOME KINDA LIGHT.

A MINOR OR A MINER? WHAT'S A...

HERE'S ONE. THEY'RE USED FOR WORKING IN VERY DEEP MINE SHAFTS WHERE THERE'S VERY LITTLE OXYGEN.

SEE? THEIR HEADS CAN BE REMOVED AND USED AS SPOTLIGHTS.

I KNEW THERE WAS MORE TO YOU THAN JUST A CUTE FACE.

WELL, WE BETTER GET GOING. WHERE DO YOU THINK THAT TUNNEL IS GOING TO LEAD US?

TUNNEL? WHY? AREN'T WE GONNA WAIT FOR SOMEONE TO COME RESCUE US? HUH?

4

SAY IT AGAIN! WHO IS THE GREATEST WRESTLER IN THE WORLD? HAH?

RENAAH! I MEAN, YOU ARE, VICKI! VICKI GLORI!!

I'M SO GOD DAMN SICK OF HEARING THAT NAME! I HATE RENA TITAÑON! I'M THE GREATEST WRESTLER THAT EVER LIVED! NOT HER!!

WELL, YOU ARE NOW ANYWAY, VICKI.

WHAT DO YOU MEAN BY THAT CRACK, CASH?

LISTEN...

...NO BODIES HAVE BEEN FOUND, BUT A WITNESS NOW CLAIMS HE SAW TITAÑON AND THE MECHANIC IN THE WAREHOUSE MINUTES BEFORE THE EXPLOSION...

CAN YOU BELIEVE IT? QUEEN RENA, DEAD? WHADAYA MAKE OF IT, VICKI? HEY, VICKI! WHERE YA GOIN'?

I NEED A SHOWER. I'LL SEE YOU GUYS IN THE MORNING.

A WITNESS CLAIMS HE SAW RENA TITAÑON AND RAND RACE'S ASSISTANT MECH ACTUALLY DIE IN A TERRORIST'S ATTACK ON A ROBOT WAREHOUSE IN CHEPAN. OFFICIALS ARE STILL UNCERTAIN WHAT THE REASON FOR THE ATTACK WAS. MS. TITAÑON WAS FORTY-EIGHT.

TITANON

... SO, THIS MECHANIC WAS A FRIEND OF YOURS, PENELOPE?

YES... A VERY CLOSE FRIEND...

MAY I MAKE A LONG DISTANCE CALL BACK HOME, HERV? CERTAIN PEOPLE MIGHT NOT HAVE HEARD THE REPORT.

SURE. I'LL GET YOU A DIRECT LINE.

8

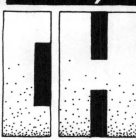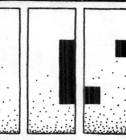

STORY THUS FAR: WORD HAS GOTTEN OUT THAT RENA AND MAGGIE HAVE BEEN KILLED IN A WAREHOUSE EXPLOSION (WE KNOW BETTER) AND A PARANOID BEAKY IS BECOMING A REAL GHOUL.

IN THE MORNING I HAVE TO TAKE A BUS TO MONTOYA TO BE WITH MAGGIE'S MOM AND RELATIVES. I'M REALLY LOOKING FORWARD TO THAT. CHRIST...

OK. I'LL GO SEE HOPEY.

I MIGHT AS WELL GO SEE HER NOW. THE SOONER THE BETTER I SUPPOSE... I'LL SEE YOU LATER, ISABEL.

DIOS TE CUIDE, PENNY.

DAMN! AFTER THIS I MAY NEVER WALK AGAIN! HOW ARE YOU DOING, MARGARET?

GEE, I DUNNO. IT'S CRAZY, BUT... I DON'T KNOW IF IT'S BECAUSE WE'VE BEEN IN THE PITCH BLACK FOR SO LONG OR IF MY MIND'S FINALLY GONE, BUT...

BUT, WHAT, SEÑORITA? WHAT...?

I-I THINK I CAN SEE YOU GUYS. YEAH... AM I CRAZY OR WHAT?

NO! YOU'RE NOT! I CAN SEE YOU, TOO!

HOORAY! THERE MUST BE AN OPENING SOMEWHERE AHEAD, LADIES! C'MON!

I DON'T GET IT, JOE. WHY ARE YOU TAKING ME TO THE WAREHOUSE THIS LATE AT NIGHT?

IT'S VERY IMPORTANT, MISTER RACE. IT'S ABOUT YOUR ASSISTANT AND LA TOÑA.

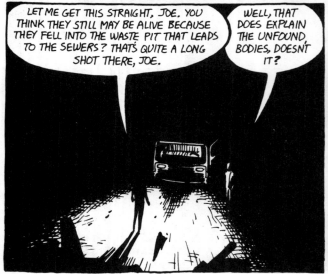

LET ME GET THIS STRAIGHT, JOE. YOU THINK THEY STILL MAY BE ALIVE BECAUSE THEY FELL INTO THE WASTE PIT THAT LEADS TO THE SEWERS? THAT'S QUITE A LONG SHOT THERE, JOE.

WELL, THAT DOES EXPLAIN THE UNFOUND BODIES, DOESN'T IT?

BUT, LOOK! THE SEWER'S BEEN FLOODED. EVEN IF THEY DID SURVIVE THE BLAST, I DON'T THINK THEY COULD HAVE...

WELL, THAT'S A CHANCE WE HAVE TO TAKE, ISN'T IT?

HOLD IT! I'M CONFUSED. A FEW DAYS AGO YOU WERE ONLY OUR TRANSPORTATION TO AND FROM CHEPAN, BUT NOW... WHY ARE YOU DOING THIS?

OK, I MIGHT AS WELL TELL YOU...

I'M SORT OF PARTLY RESPONSIBLE FOR WHAT HAS HAPPENED. I WAS WORKING WITH THE TERRORISTS WHO BLEW UP THE ROBOT WAREHOUSE...

IT WAS AN ACCIDENT! BELIEVE ME, NO ONE WAS SUPPOSED TO GET HURT! IT WAS ONLY TO SHOW DOCTOR BEAKY THAT WE THE PEOPLE OF CHEPAN CANNOT BE PUSHED AROUND...

"THEY WERE ONLY DESTROYING EMPTY BUILDINGS THAT WERE OWNED BY BEAKY. HECK, THOSE TERRORISTS ARE JUST A HANDFUL OF COLLEGE STUDENTS WHO WERE TIRED OF BEAKY AND HIS WEALTH AND WHO JUST HAPPENED TO GET A HOLD OF SOME EXPLOSIVES. I HELPED THEM BECAUSE I KNEW IT WAS A GOOD CAUSE..."

SO, IF YOU THINK THIS IS SOME WILD-GOOSE CHASE, YOU CAN WALK AWAY RIGHT NOW. BUT IF YOU CAN IMAGINE THE TWO WOMEN SOMEWHERE OUT THERE ALIVE AND BREATHING, CRYING OUT FOR HELP, THEN YOU CAN MEET ME AT THE ROCKET HANGERS IN THE MORNING AT SIX. THINK ABOUT IT.

AW, WHAT THE HELL HAPPENED? WHERE DID WE GO WRONG?

RENA! I CAN'T SEE YOU GUYS ANY MORE!

I... CAN'T UNDERSTAND IT. FOR A FEW MINUTES THERE, WE COULD ACTUALLY SEE... THEN...

OH, KAKA!

DON'T CRY, MARGARET. WE'RE NOT FINISHED YET. WE'LL GET OUT OF HERE...

C'MON, LADIES. WE'LL SLEEP IT OFF. WE CAN START AGAIN IN A FEW HOURS.

Z Z

SHIT... WE'RE NEVER GETTING OUT OF HERE... MAYBE THIS TUNNEL IS LEADING US TO HELL...

MAYBE... ZZZ

3

WHAT A DAY THIS HAS BEEN. IT STILL FEELS LIKE A DREAM. I DON'T THINK I COULD EVER LAST ANOTHER LIKE IT.

TWO O'CLOCK. DIDN'T REALIZE IT WAS SO LATE. HOPEY'S PROBABLY NOT EVEN UP. WAIT, THE DOOR'S BEEN LEFT OPEN.

HOPEY? ARE YOU UP?

HOPEY? IT'S ME PENNY. ARE YOU...

THEN, IT'S TRUE?

Z

MARGARET!

WHADDAYA WANT?

MARGARET! COME ON! COME ON OUT!

RENA? WHAT...?

134

YEAH... I'M REALLY SORRY ABOUT THIS. I REALLY SHOULDN'T HAVE MADE YOU COME ALONG. THIS IS MY PROBLEM AND I...

HEY, IF I DIDN'T WANT TO COME, I WOULDN'T BE HERE.

BUT, THIS ALL SEEMS SO HOPELESS! IT'S A BILLION TO ONE SHOT...

REMEMBER WHAT JOE SAID? PEOPLE HAVE BEEN KNOWN TO LIVE IN THOSE TUNNELS FOR LONG PERIODS OF TIME. SO THERE'S STILL THAT CHANCE.

YOU'RE INCREDIBLE. WHAT WOULD I DO WITHOUT YOU, DOT?

I KNOW, I KNOW...

QUIÑA CHASCARRILLO'S HOME IN MONTOYA...

SPEEDY'S JUST A LITTLE DRUNK, IZZY. WE'LL TAKE CARE OF HIM.

OK, THANKS, LICHA.

HEY! DON'T TALK TO THAT BITCH IN THERE! SHE USED THE ROPES TO WIN THE BELT FROM TITAÑON, MAN!

SORRY ABOUT MY BROTHER. NOW, AS I WAS SAYING... I'M REALLY A BIG FAN OF YOURS. I WATCH YOU WRESTLE ON TV ALL THE TIME. I REALLY ENJOY YOUR ATOMIC PILEDRIVER.

YEAH, WELL, WE CAN'T TALK ABOUT THAT RIGHT NOW, I'M IN MOURNING FOR TWO PEOPLE, Y'KNOW...

FIRST, I HEAR ABOUT QUEEN RENA... THEN ALL OF A SUDDEN I HEAR THAT MY LITTLE NIECE WAS WITH HER IN THE HOOPLA.

I REALIZE YOU MUST BE IN REAL PAIN.

8

DAMN STRAIGHT! RENA TITAÑON TAUGHT ME EVERYTHING I KNOW. AND IN OUR FUEDING DAYS, THERE WAS ONLY ONE GAL WHO COULD SEND ME FLYING OVER THAT TOP ROPE O THOSE HUNDRED TIMES. SHE WAS THE GREATEST...

...SO, IN HER (AND SHRIMP'S) HONOR, VICKI GLORI, CHAMPION OF CHAMPIONS IS, Y'ALL HEARD IT HERE FIRST, IS GOING CLEAN. NO KICKING, NO BITING, NO GOUGING, NO MORE ATOMIC PILEDRIVER!

THIS CALLS FOR A DRINK, CHAMP.

HELLO, HOPEY. HOW ARE YOU?

HELLO.

HI. LET'S GO TO THE RESTROOM, TERRY.

THIS PLUMBING, I SWEAR... HOW ARE YOU DOING, HOPEY? ARE YOU FEELING BETTER?

I'M FINE, I'M FINE! I'M JUST GOING CRAZY STAYING ALONE IN THAT APARTMENT. IZZY OFFERED TO LET ME MOVE IN WITH HER. I'M THINKING ABOUT IT...

HMF! I OFFERED YOU THE SAME DEAL, BUT... WHAT ABOUT YOU AND I, HOPEY? YOU THINK NOW THAT... YOU KNOW...

YOU AND I COULD NEVER BE AS CLOSE AS WE ONCE WERE, TERRY. YOU COULD NEVER HANDLE IT WHEN THE SHIT CAME DOWN.

YEAH? WELL, WHAT ABOUT MAGGIE? SHE WAS NEVER YOUR TYPE AND YOU KNOW IT!

OH, OH, OH! AND YOU WERE? YOU... AGHHH! NEVER MIND!

YOU JUST HAD HER AROUND BECAUSE SHE'D DO ANYTHING YOU'D FUCKING WANT HER TO!

PUT A BIG LOAD OF SHIT IN YOUR MOUTH AND CHOKE ON IT, WILL YOU, TERRY?

HELLO, HOPEY. HOW ARE YOU?

HELLO.

AH, SHADDAP!

TSK! POOR HOPEY.

140

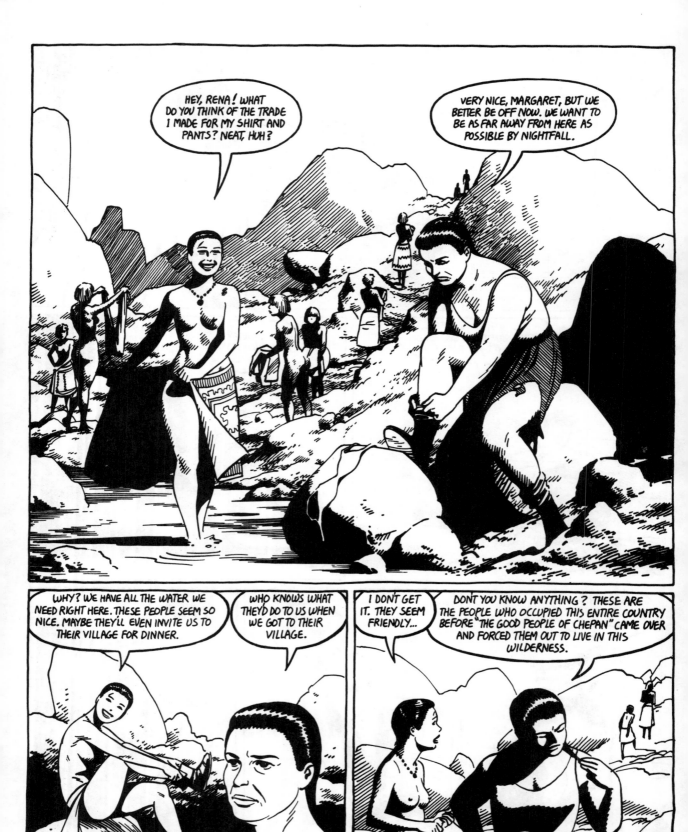

142

144

15

145

HEH... YEAH... WELL, WE GOTTA GET GOING NOW...

HEY!

WAIT! THERE'S SOME BEER IN THE REFRIGERATOR. YOU WANNA WATCH TV OR SOMETHING?

UH, NO. WE BETTER GO. MAYBE YOU SHOULD REST OR SOMETHING. THANKS ANYWAY.

HEY! I WANTED A BEER, MAN!

OK... SEE YA.

BUT YOU HATE YOUR MOTHER, HOPEY! I DON'T GET IT! AND YOUR HAIR...

DAFFY. I'LL BE BACK IN A FEW DAYS.

IT'S NOT LIKE I'M GOING TO LIVE THERE FOR GOOD. I HAVEN'T LOST ALL MY MARBLES... YET. BUT I DO NEED A VACATION FROM THIS CRAZED TOWN AND ITS INHABITANTS. AT LEAST MY MOM'S BEEN NUTS ALL HER LIFE. NOT JUST RECENTLY...

DON'T LET YOUR MOTHER'S NEW BOY-FRIEND RAPE YOU, EH, HOPITA?

(SNIFF) I WISH MAGGIE WAS HERE AND EVERYTHING WAS BACK TO NORMAL.

SO DO I. THEN MAYBE EVERYBODY WOULD STOP ACTING SO SERIOUS.

LET'S SEE, NOW... MAGGIE AND RENA ARE STILL BELIEVED TO BE DEAD, BUT JOE, RACE AND DOT HAVE OTHER IDEAS AS THEY'VE GONE OUT LOOKING FOR THEM IN OUTER CHEPAN. OH, YEAH, DOCTOR BEAKY CAPTURED THE TERRORISTS WHO SUPPOSEDLY KILLED OUR HEROINES AND HAS ORDERED TO HAVE THEM EXECUTED, SO THE PEOPLE OF CHEPAN ARE REVOLTING. BACK AT HOME, A SAD HOPEY HAS DECIDED TO STAY WITH HER MOTHER FOR A WHILE, AND VICKI GLORI HAS GONE CLEAN. GET ALL THAT? WELL, THAT'S OK, BECAUSE IT ENDS IN THIS ONE. I PROMISE.

MECHANICS

PART 6

84 JAIME 85

HATE TO TELL YOU THIS, JOE, BUT THIS IS OUR LAST STOP BEFORE WE HEAD ON BACK HOME.

WHAT?

La Chata

148

149

156

LAS MUJÉRES PERDIDAS

THE LOST WOMEN

BY JAIME 83-84

THE END